NORTH OF 55°

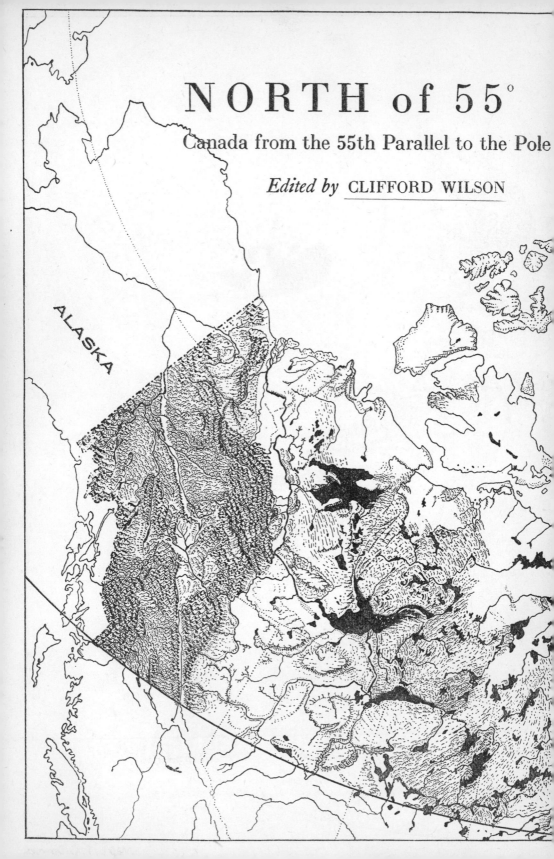

NORTH of 55°

Canada from the 55th Parallel to the Pole

Edited by CLIFFORD WILSON

ALASKA

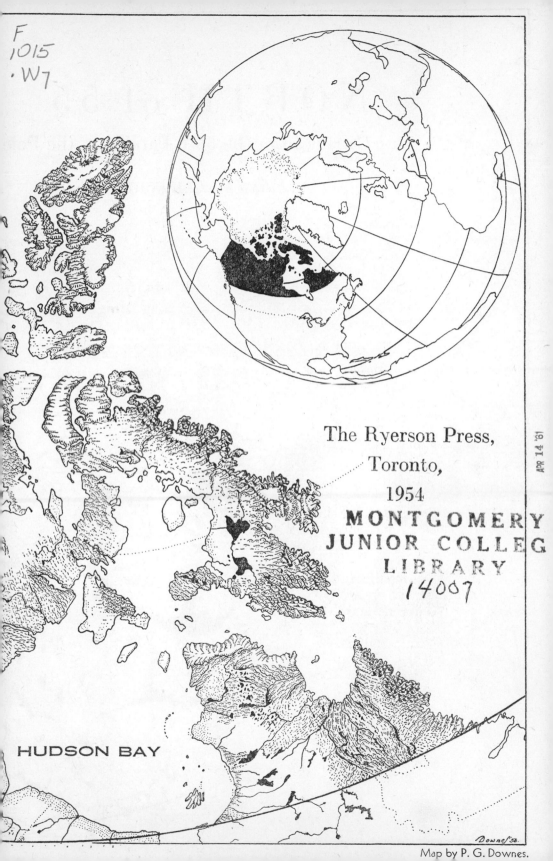

The Ryerson Press,

Toronto,

1954

HUDSON BAY

Downes '52.

Map by P. G. Downes.

Contents

14007

Illustrations

Maps and Diagrams

Editor to Reader

THIS book is about Canada today north of the 55th parallel—an easy one to remember because it cuts the four western Provinces roughly in half and divides Hudson Bay from James Bay. It's a book for laymen, written by specialists. That, of course, is not an easy thing for specialists to do. They would much rather write for their fellow experts. Each one of them knows his subject so well, he finds it hard to believe that what to him are perfectly simple statements may not be understood by the average reader.

The only non-expert in the list of sixteen contributors is the editor, and it has been part of his task to suggest what approach the authors might make to their subjects (so that the lay reader may the more easily follow them) and also to simplify some of their more technical descriptions. Happily, most of the authors agreed with his suggested changes; but others did so grudgingly, and still others didn't agree with them at all. There is such a thing, they pointed out, as over-simplification. Another difficulty that plagued both author and editor was keeping each chapter down to a reasonable length. Three thousand words was the required limit, but of course everyone exceeded it, and every manuscript had to be cut and cut again—a painful process for all concerned.

Some of the chapters, such as those on climate and flora, will be full of surprises for a lot of people. And so may the one on the R.C.M.P. If you picture the northern duties of Canada's famous Mounted Police as being full of danger and excitement, you will have to revise your ideas when you read Staff-Sgt. Kearney's account of policing the Northwest Territories and the Yukon. We have no doubt that this author's own Arctic experiences have been flavoured with much more than the traditional "Mountie" activities than he writes of here—such as bringing out the Eskimo murderers from the Belchers in 1941. But his description of the prosaic duties of the Force in the North will serve as an antidote to popular emphasis on the picturesque.

In each chapter an effort has been made to stay away from dry statistics, and to present the facts about the North as interestingly and as readably as possible. The headings have also been chosen to get away from the usual "Geography," "Minerals," "Flora," and so on; and chapters about natural resources have been interspersed with some about human activities.

Today the North is very much in the public eye. For the average Canadian, looking at the North is something like looking from a mountain top across an almost unknown but vastly inviting landscape, stretching out to the horizon, full of mystery and beauty, adventure and untold wonders. All of these, we hope, you will look for, and find in these pages; and, as Joseph Conrad says, perhaps also that glimpse of truth for which you have forgotten to ask.

CLIFFORD WILSON

Winnipeg, March 1954

Margaret R. Montgomery is a geographer and clima-
tologist with the Defence Research Board of Canada.
Among the better known expeditions to the North in which
she has taken part were the 8,000-mile "Flight Cariberg" of
1948 and the Baird Baffin Island expedition of 1950. She
has also lectured in geography at McMaster University.

The Face of the Land

by M. R. MONTGOMERY

FRONTIERS are always a challenge, and for Canada today
this challenge lies in the far horizons of that stern and
still-unconquered northland whose limits stretch almost
from sea to sea, and if not quite "from the river" at least
"unto the ends of the earth."

To the first settlers pressing west from the forested
areas of the eastern seaboard, the Prairies appeared as a
strange and desolate land where civilized man could never
live, and which lay as a hostile barrier between them and the
forests of the Pacific coast. These broad expanses of grass-
land suggested no splendid future of grainfields, ranches and
cities, but only an unfriendly and dangerous country where
no one thought to settle and where men congratulated themselves on their skill and good fortune once they succeeded in
crossing safely to the other side. Today we are almost in
that same stage in our attitude toward the North. It is

a rugged land, demanding for its development techniques and equipment which we are only now slowly developing, and imposing on those who would conquer it a pattern of life different from any we have followed in the past. Yet, the farther we penetrate, and the more we know its character, the richer appears to be its promised contribution to the nation's future wealth.

Most of us are accustomed to maps which display the whole of Canada on a single sheet, and as a result we sometimes find it difficult to realize the truly enormous size of the country. Those who travel it from east to west get some idea of the extent of the settled areas of the mainland when, after a journey of some 3500 to 4000 miles, or five days and nights of continuous train travel from St. John or Halifax, they finally arrive in Vancouver. Relatively few have a similar chance to experience personally the comparable vastness of the northern regions. So large is the country, in fact, and so vast its unexplored and unsurveyed areas, that not until the coming of the airplane and the development of aerial photography could sufficient information be collected to permit any detailed mapping of the North.

In the vicinity of the 55th parallel, which lies approximately at the southern limits of Hudson Bay, Canada could contain the Eurasian continent at the same latitude, from the west coast of Ireland to the tributaries of the River Ob in Siberia (see Map 1). In north-south extent the whole Dominion equals approximately the distance in Europe between the southern peninsulas of Greece and the northern capes of Norway.

The first characteristic of the Canadian North is its vastness; the second is its emptiness, the sparseness of human population which has resulted in large measure from the severity of its climate. Into the Arctic and sub-Arctic areas of this continent could be fitted several of the larger

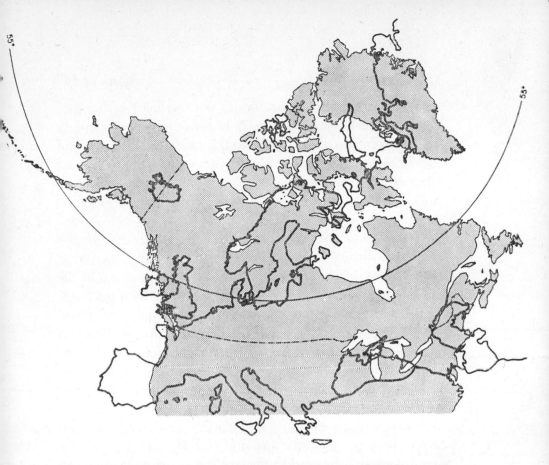

On this map of northern North America, the cartographer has outlined Europe and part of Asia on the same scale and in the same latitudes.

heavily-populated countries of Europe. Copenhagen lies roughly in about the same latitude as Churchill, Murmansk is about as far north as Aklavik, and Edinburgh, Oslo and Helsinki are located in the latitudes of Whitehorse and Ungava Bay. But more severe Canadian climate has helped to delay and hinder settlement, so that while the northern European countries are well populated and have become centres of actual and potential wealth, much of northern Canada remains predominantly a waste and empty land.

The vastness of the country and the sparseness of its population have meant that settlements are widely separated from each other, and communications with the outside world

are difficult and often undependable.   Much of this difficulty results from the nature of the terrain whose natural
ruggedness has been greatly increased in many areas by the
vast sheets of ice, several thousand feet thick in places,
which covered the northern part of the Canadian mainland
and much of the Arctic Archipelago during the last ice age.

The Shield

Just as the landscapes of Europe present considerable
variety, so also does each of the geographic regions of the
vast Canadian northland possess its own very definite
character.   The largest of these regions is that rocky
glaciated area which extends westward from the Labrador
coast to the broken chain of lakes stretching from Lake
Superior to Great Bear Lake.   It is known as the *Precambrian*, *Laurentian*, or *Canadian Shield*, and is a land of very
ancient mountains which, long before the last ice age, had
been worn down to their roots by the action of wind and
snow, rain and rivers.   Looked at in a general way or from
an aircraft the country appears fairly level, having no
outstandingly high mountains and no exceptionally deep
valleys.   Its most noticeable general feature is its monotony,
a sameness which makes it very difficult for the traveller to
pick out any distinctive landmarks by which to guide himself.   Looked at in detail, however, the terrain is extremely
rough: hill after hill, valley after valley, all approximately
the same height or depth, the hills worn by ice and by time,
the valleys filled with lakes, swamps, or glacial debris.

During the last Glacial Period, the ice sheets scoured the
ground, removing the layers of overburden which covered
the bedrock, deepening existing lakes and river beds, transporting rocks and boulders far from their original location,
and grinding much of the rock and soil into a fine powder.
While the ice sheets were active and moving, this burden of

glacial debris was carried forward and deposited around their outer edges in the form of great moraines and boulder fields. When the ice became stagnant and finally melted, it dropped its heavy load wherever it happened to disintegrate, leaving mounds of boulder clay, or "drift" as it is often called, scattered haphazardly over the country.

In the North where precipitation is light and annual temperatures low, erosion is an extremely slow process. The effects of glaciation thus remain very clearly marked on the landscape and are easy to distinguish in the areas beyond the treeline, particularly on that great triangular stretch of country known as "the Barrens" which lies north and northwest from Churchill between Hudson Bay and the northern coast.

Some of the commonest indications of glacial action are:
Boulder fields—Wide stretches of ground covered by a mantle of rough boulders of all sizes, over which travel on foot may be very difficult and travel by vehicle impossible.
Erratic boulders—Individual rocks, often of considerable size, deposited by the ice far from their place of origin.
Moraines—Hills or ridges of rock and clay debris which mark the ends or edges of old glaciers.
Eskers—Long, narrow ridges, usually of sand or gravel, formed by streams which once flowed through the ice cap. As the ice melted, these beds of river sediment were deposited on the land beneath. They often stretch for many miles across the country like winding railroad embankments.
Drumlins—Low hills of glacial debris, usually somewhat elliptical in form. In some areas they are very numerous and are all aligned in the direction that the ice under which they were formed was moving at the time they were deposited.

Over the Canadian Shield as a whole, the most widespread legacy from the ice age is the disturbed drainage

pattern of which a small fragment is shown in the eastern
section of Map II. The scattered patches of soil which
have remained or developed since the disappearance of the ice
are too few and too thin to hold much moisture. Down-
ward seepage and underground drainage are also severely
limited because of the hard, rocky surface, and as a result
water collects in every hollow and depression, forming
innumerable lakes of all sizes, shapes and depths. These
afford excellent landing fields for aircraft but make cross-
country travel in summer almost impossible except by canoe.
"Drift" has blocked many of the pre-glacial river valleys,
forming dunes behind which the streams spread out to
become shallow boulder-strewn lakes, drained in some cases
by two or more rivers, each flowing in a different direction.
True rivers are comparatively rare, the majority being
merely a chain of lakes which drain into each other over a
series of rapids, and which frequently double back on themselves many times before reaching a main channel to the sea.
Many a portage and many a detour is the lot of those who
would travel such waterways.

As the ice retreated, much of the melt water collected in
vast sheets along its edge, behind barriers of glacial debris
and stagnant ice, or in the deepened basins of pre-glacial
lakes. Today many of these great lakes have completely
drained away and disappeared, but the broad stretches of
water-deposited sediments which formed their beds are
familiar to us as the Clay Belts, the most famous of which is
the one centred around Cochrane in Northern Ontario.
Along the boundaries of the Shield the shrunken remnants of
other post-glacial lakes form the continent's largest water-
bodies: the Great Lakes, Lake Winnipeg and the larger lakes
of the Northwest—Athabasca, Great Slave and Great Bear,
the last two ranking next in size after Lakes Superior, Huron
and Michigan.

Along the shores of these lakes can often be traced a long series of terraces, or sand and gravel beaches, which marked the progressive lowering of the water-level as the ice sheets disappeared, reducing not only the source of the water but also removing many of the barrier dams.   In certain areas the wind has drifted the sand of these old beaches into dunes, which are often sparsely covered by arctic plants.

North of that zone of transition known as the treeline, the hard rocky character of the country is exposed in all its ruggedness, its only cover being the scattered patches of stunted tundra vegetation which shelter in the crevices or spread thinly over the plains and northern "meadows." South from the treeline, the increasing denseness of the evergreen forests softens the uncompromising aspect of the terrain, but even here, rocky outcrops and stretches of muskeg betray the rough-grained nature of the land beneath.

In a very general sense the Shield has the form of a saucer, being lowest around Hudson Bay, its central point, and highest along the edges.   The slope of the land is so gradual that it has little directional influence on any but the larger rivers.   The smaller streams continue to wander hap-hazardly, misleading any traveller who relies on them to help him keep his bearings.

Around Hudson Bay the land has been gradually rising from the sea since the disappearance of the ice sheet, and along its southern coasts the hard basement rocks of the Shield have been overlain by wide, swampy mud flats. Travel over this poorly drained area by means other than canoe is difficult, except in winter, although a certain free-dom of movement might be possible in all seasons along the series of ancient beaches which extend in parallel ridges inland from the present shore.   The rivers and the sea form the main "highways" but the even coastline and the shallow offshore waters provide little in the way of good harbours.

The Interior Lowlands

To the west, between the Shield and the eastern borders of the Cordillera* lies that northern extension of the Great Plains usually referred to as the *Interior Lowlands*. Rocky outcrops are rare, as the soil and overburden which cover the basement rocks are usually of considerable depth. The general slope of the land is towards the north, governing the direction of North America's second longest river, the Mackenzie. Down this river explorers pushed their way to the Arctic Ocean, and along its banks mainland settlements first penetrated into the North. Unfortunately for the development of the Arctic in both North America and Eurasia, the main rivers which form the first and most important routes of travel and trade, flow away from civilization and towards the ice-bound polar seas.

The low evaporation characteristic of the cool summers conserves the light rainfall, and together with the presence of good soil cover, provides a mantle of spruce, birch and poplar forest instead of the grasses characteristic of the Prairies to the south. A certain amount of agriculture has been possible and this in turn, in spite of the sparseness of the population, has given to the scattered settlements a more permanent character than is found in most of the mining settlements of the Shield. These latter are rarely able to survive once their immediate supply of ore is exhausted and either become ghost towns or, like Sherridon in Manitoba, must find a new site for their existence. At some settlements of the Interior Plains, experimental agriculture is being carried on, and it is interesting to realize that it is in comparable sub-Arctic areas of Siberia, that Russia has achieved the remarkable agricultural developments which have received so much publicity.

---

*Cordillera is the name applied to the complex systems of mountain ranges along the west coast of North and South America.

With the existence of soil cover, it might be expected that the drainage of the northern section of the Interior Lowlands would be less disturbed than that of the Shield, and, to a large degree, it is. However, all but the top layers of the soil remain permanently frozen throughout the year, forming an almost rock-like base under the surface layers and preventing water from percolating downwards as it does in more temperate climates. As a result, much of the surface remains spongy throughout the summer, and in many areas, swamps are the rule rather than the exception. The unstable surface conditions resulting from this thawing and freezing of the top layers, combined with the permanent frost conditions below, present endless difficulties to the engineer and builder.

Glaciation has not disturbed the drainage pattern of the Lowlands to the same degree as on the Shield, and the boundary between these two major regions shows clearly on a map because of the contrasting character of the lakes and rivers.

The Cordillera

To the west of the Interior Plains lies the *Cordillera Region* which includes the high mountainous "backbone" of the North American continent, as well as the foothills to the east of it. It comprises almost the entire area of northern British Columbia, the whole of the Yukon and much of Alaska, and contains such peaks as Mount Logan, Canada's highest and North America's second highest mountain, and Mount Robson, the giant of the Canadian Rockies.* The mountains reach their most majestic heights along the Pacific Coast where extensive ice fields and peaks over 15,000 feet are fairly common. East and north from this, the altitudes tend to diminish, but the country still remains very rugged, and penetration is difficult in the extreme.

*Mount Logan rises 19,850 feet, Mount Robson 12,972 feet.

The region has been heavily glaciated, and many of the high jagged peaks and ridges are still covered by extensive snow and ice fields.   During the ice age, glaciers deepened the channels through which they flowed, and when they retreated, left behind not only moraines of glacial debris, but also steep-walled valleys with broad level floors.   Through these flow great mountain rivers, fed in many cases by the melt water of ice fields at higher altitudes.   These streams tend to meander from side to side across their valleys and, with their heavy load of sand, silt or gravel, they often build up shifting bars which divide their channels into many branches and so develop what is known as a "braided stream."   Their water levels can fluctuate from a mere trickle in early autumn to a roaring springtime torrent (such as destroyed so many bridges on the Canol Road) which leaves the valley floors sodden and muddy throughout most of the summer.

Along the Pacific Coast, powerful glaciers flowing down to the sea from the high lands of the interior carved great steep-sided fiords similar to those of Norway.   These inlets, with their sheer rocky walls rising hundreds of feet from the sea, reach their most spectacular development in northern British Columbia.

The most striking single feature of the Cordilleran region is the Rocky Mountain Trench which extends as a straight, relatively narrow, highwalled depression, northwest from the State of Washington to the valley of the Liard River at about 60°N.   The Rocky Mountains form its eastern wall, while a series of ranges of the Cassiar and Omineca Mountains bound it on the west.   Along its floor flow the Fraser, and the Parsnip and Finlay which join to form the Peace and escape to the east through a gap in the Rockies.

In the more southerly areas of the northern Cordillera, spruce forests cover the valleys and lower slopes.   As one

goes north, however, this Alpine treeline drops to increasingly lower altitudes and tree growth is finally limited
to a few straggling willows and alders along the valley
streams.

Settlements are found in the main river valleys, many of
them being located to serve the needs of those engaged in
placer mining for gold.   They depend on either air or water
transport from the outside to supply their needs.   Until the
construction of the Alaska Highway and the chain of airfields which it serves, all supplies in this difficult area were
either moved inland by way of the narrow-gauge railway
from Skagway to Whitehorse, or else transported by boat
and barge along the main waterways such as the Liard, the
Stikine and, above all, the Yukon.

The Arctic Archipelago

Situated north of the Canadian mainland is the great
triangle of the Arctic Archipelago with its apex at Cape
Columbia (87°07′N.), Peary's jumping-off point on his
poleward journey.   Although containing many local variations of terrain, the islands are all, with the exception of the
two northernmost, Axel Heiberg and Ellesmere, fragments
of a vast plateau which slopes upwards from relatively low
elevations in the south and west to heights of over 5,000 feet
above sea level along the eastern coasts.   By contrast, the
two northern islands are crossed by great ranges of mountains whose peaks, rising in places to 12,000 feet, are among
the highest in eastern North America.   The western
islands escaped glaciation, but much of their surface is
covered by frost-shattered rock fragments, and great slopes
of weathered rock lie against the foot of all cliffs and hills.
The higher eastern islands bordering Baffin Bay were better
located to receive a sufficient supply of the precipitation that
is so essential to the formation of ice caps.   On these islands

the effects of this ice cover are everywhere in evidence. Relics of the great ice sheets which once covered the country still remain on the higher areas, covering the greater part of Devon, Ellesmere and Axel Heiberg. Great glacier tongues flow from these caps down to the sea and continue to-day, on a smaller scale, the scouring process of the larger parent sheet which not so long ago carved the magnificent fiords that fringe Baffin Bay and the north-eastern Arctic coast.

The whole area lies north of the treeline, and therefore its vegetation is limited to the low tundra growth of the arctic summer. Its population is limited to scattered Eskimo encampments and to the tiny coastal trading settlements, weather stations and police detachments.

Except for the differences in vegetation and the long enduring effects of glaciation, landscapes in the North resemble those found in other parts of the country. Instead of a single type of landscape "typical of the Arctic," almost every type of terrain can be found in this vast region: mountains and fiords, low hills and shallow valleys, meandering rivers and swift mountain streams, stretches of sand dunes and areas of swamp, sea cliffs and low coastal flats, all typical of their part of the North and each presenting its own problems to settlement, travel or development. In the final analysis it is the climate, both past and present, which has effectively determined the character of the Canadian North and, by surrounding it with ice-filled seas, has enforced on the region a long isolation which modern needs and communications are only now beginning to relieve.

Prentice G. Downes, a graduate of Harvard, is a teacher in geomorphology and history at a boys' school in Belmont, Mass. He has done a great deal of canoe travel in northern Manitoba and Saskatchewan and the Northwest Territories, and he has made a study of northern literature and archives. During the recent war he did cartographic work at the Institute of Geographic Exploration at Harvard. His Sleeping Island, *about the Nueltin Lake country north of Manitoba, was published in 1943.*

First Comers

by P. G. DOWNES

No other comparable area of the earth's surface presents such an extraordinary record of sustained exploration as Canada north of 55°. Where else may one find an articulate record of nearly four hundred years and yet a record still far from complete? It is like a vast and intricate tapestry of which the fabric, though limited by an ultimate framework, bears within itself both complex and simple designs, in which some of the individual threads are worn and dim and yet others are live and glowing. These patterns of human endeavour and accomplishment follow the most wondrous convolutions of the human spirit and, regardless of their brevity, length and colour, contribute each to the grand design, the completion of which still awaits generations to come.

As you look back through the centuries, you will find that this mighty epic is a truly staggering edifice of the written word, and yet even this is but a small fragment of the total story.   You will find also that it is really a distilled and particular reflection of the whole historical drama of western European civilization in these same four hundred years.   Like that too, though displaced in time, there is an immense chronological substructure which you can but dimly see and which in large part still remains to be un-covered.   The exploration of this vast and silent area is known to us today only since the first voyage of Frobisher in 1576.   Before that, however, lies an enormous period of time in which its secrets were probed and revealed with quite as heroic human effort, fear, triumph and despair.

Conservatively, for at least five thousand years some-one has been exploring some part of Canada's far north. That the written evidence does not exist does not deny the fact nor the human struggle.   It is curious justice that now, as the obvious geographical exploration is drawing to a finite close, this other end of the historical record is at the dawn of its real revelation.

Though the story of the thousands of years of exploring before the white man is dim indeed, traces do exist and the sequence of this truly first, great, man-adventure into the huge new world of taiga* and tundra is only now beginning to be understood.   Ironically, the instrument for this has, within the last six years, sprung directly from that devised to destroy man in the Asiatic fastness somewhere from which he came to the new world.   The Carbon-14 tech-nique through which the archaeologist may discover the accurate and dated history of the yesterday is a step-child of the atomic bomb.

Whose eyes were those which first searched the crum-bling, rotting mass of the great continental ice-sheet? Whose

---

*Taiga is the swampy region of coniferous forest south of the tundra.

hands fashioned arrow point and spear? Whence did he come into the ever-widening forest and barrens of the Canadian north after his first crossing of the Bering Sea land-bridge? Were his words those of the Athapascan, the Algonkian, the Eskimoan tongues we know today? Was he of a ghost legion whose only memorials are the strange, fluted arrow points mixed with extinct species of bison, sloth or mammoth? These threads in the tapestry await the interpretation of searchers of the North to come. The evidence is there, and probably every white explorer since— whether he has travelled the great river routes by canoe, or the horizon-bound barrens by foot, whether stepped ashore from His or Her Majesty's ship, or has been today gently eased from a helicopter—sooner or later, from the mute witness of a few blackened heath stones, a splinter of quartz, or the elaborate foundations of a "Tunit" ruin, has said to himself, "Someone has been here before me."

Indeed, one of the most fascinating aspects of the whole great saga is exactly this persistent phrase. The deeper one probes, the more insistent the refrain for, in the way of the human ego, fame and credit adhere only in proportion to the preserved and published record, not in the actuality of the accomplishment. No better example of this do we find than in our accepted "first" into this area. For behind Martin Frobisher's trips to "Meta Incognita," Baffin Island, lie the shadowy ghosts of the Norseman Karlsefni and his followers almost six hundred years before.

But it is with Frobisher of 1576-8 that the drama, as we presently understand it in detail, unfolds, and it is in his three voyages that we can see the outline of the larger design to be followed in part or whole for roughly the next two hundred years. First, there is the beckoning, golden illusion so tempting to a vigorous post-Renaissance, maritime Europe: a western route to Cathay, China, Japan, the Spice

Isles, India.   Second is the claiming and charting of those new islands and land masses, the new world itself, which were found obstructing the pursuit of the dream.   Third occurs the alternating economic underwriting of the dream by private and sovereign subsidy; and last, in the disillusionment of the dream, the effort to salvage some tangible reward.   All of this is still valid today; only the mechanics have changed, and the dream and the fact have been realized.

If today those ancient Odysseys, preserved in antique rhetoric, have taken unto themselves a legendary, fairy-story and heroic unreality—Frobisher in his tiny *Gabriel*, Davis in his thirty-five ton *Moonshine*, Weymouth, Henry Hudson, Button, Baffin, Bylot, Foxe and James—the simple truth is that they were just that.   They *were* heroes.   They chose to seek a challenge clothed not in the verdure and warmth of a Caribbean main, nor the gentle slope of a mid-Atlantic coastal plain, but killing cold and the jagged coastal battlements of a thousand mile Baffin Island range, or the grim Torngats of Labrador rising straight from the sea in repelling, sombre grandeur.

If you think we are being unfashionably romantic, go to Churchill, Manitoba, today.   Gaze out over the sullen, grey sea.   Project yourself backward three hundred and thirty-four years.   The bitter winter has passed.   One-by-one sixty of your shipmates have died festering with scurvy, exposure, gangrenous frost-bite.   Three only of you are left. No other human being has even been seen in this barren, empty, aching land.   Yet, you still have the courage to embark in a boat not much larger than a sailing dory and you sail it all the way back to Denmark; but not before you were able to write in your journal: "Herewith, goodnight to all the world; and my soul in the hand of God—*Jens Munck*."

The Great Dream, a practical northwest passage, lingered on well into the middle of the eighteenth century.

In the latter half, the first real concept of the staggering immensity of the great northern continental barrier was established. Many and singular designs and threads had been woven into our tapestry from the high tide of Eliza-bethan adventure to the more prosaic mercantilism of the Georges. At our selected moment, now, almost exactly a century had passed since those volatile and agile "Caesars of the Wilderness," Des Groseilliers and Radisson had seduced "the Company of Adventurers of England trading into Hudson's Bay" to permanent lodgement on those low, mosquito-ridden shores. One hundred years, and still no one knew what really lay within the continental arc north of 55°.*

It is as if by dramatic connivance of the fates that this great age of white exploration should be terminated with the unlocking of the interior, the ending of the dream, and the most brilliant individual performance in all North American exploration. There is a certain poetic justice, too, that its author should be a servant of the Great Com-pany even at that moment embarking upon its second century of continuous operation in the north.

On July 17, 1771, Samuel Hearne, after two abortive attempts, each in themselves remarkable exploratory feats, stood on the polar rim of the continent. On foot, in com-pany with his Chipewyan-Cree friend and guide Maton-abbee, this lone and resolute white man had traversed the mysterious, unknown, immense world of the far northern land-mass. No matter his faulty astronomical observations, to this hour Hearne's trip from present day Churchill to the mouth of the Coppermine River and back again remains the most remarkable exploratory achievement by a single in-dividual in the new world. To this very day, portions of that track still await the foot of the next white man. From that day to this, the duplication of even fragments of his

*The explorations of Henry Kelsey (1690-92), the La Vérendryes (1732-49), Anthony Henday (1754) and William Stewart (1714-15) were in the first three cases south of our area and in the latter no exact geographical data are known.

trek has been sufficient to bring fame and renown to lesser
men.   It is fitting, too, that his first public notice should
have occurred with the delineation of the northwestern
continental margin by that master of the global seas, Captain
Cook.

But now, great events had taken place "outside," and in
the far north the shadows of things to come are more often
the reflections of things which have passed.   New France
had bowed to Britain, and the southern approaches now
open, a trickle and then a flood of adventurers from Montreal
pressed northward into the fur-rich, virgin wilderness of the
high latitude forests.   It was these men who were to
hesitantly coalesce into the North West Company out of
whose bitter economic struggle with the Hudson's Bay
Company not only great explorations in themselves developed but the logistic mechanics for those of others.

First into the new sub-arctic arena was the irascible
Peter Pond, no ordinary fur trader but one who had been
touched with the dream.   There, at the delta of the Athabasca in 1778, he laid the plans which Alexander Mackenzie
translated into geographic reality, the exploration of the
River of Disappointment—the Mackenzie—in 1789, and
the first crossing of the continent four years later.   But
even here, ghosts linger, for back of these two hover the dim
figure of a "Lewis Primo" (Louis Primeau) and a Francois
Beaulieu whom time and silence have almost buried.   Out
of this struggle grew the surveys of Turnor, Fidler and
Thompson, fixed for all time upon the constantly revised
and increasingly detailed map of the indefatigable Arrow-
smith far away in London.   Out of this were born the
permanent bases from and to which far northern adventurers
have set forth and returned down to the present day.

With the first half of the nineteenth century, the assault
takes a different cast both in objective, locale, mode and

genesis.   It is this age which even today colours much of the popular concept of the north.   For this was the turn of truly Arctic exploration.   Popular appeal was still attracted by the magic words "Northwest Passage" but the real motivation was much more within the framework of the age itself.   This was the period in western culture when science, as we know it today, was first in the ascendant, and particularly it was that phase in which infant science was not only supremely confident in its discovery of the rational and logical, but was omnivorous in its appetite for physical evidence from which to prove its budding hypotheses and from which to create new ones.   It was the age of great collecting—be it animal, vegetable, mineral, vocabularies, customs or cartographic outlines of coast and cape.   The north supplied wonderfully well this challenge that all physical matter, above, under, and on the earth, be known and classified.   Out of this were born the elaborate ventures sponsored in the main by the British Admiralty under its secretary Sir John Barrow, and out of it came much of our basic knowledge of Canada north of 55° particularly where washed by the Polar Sea.

One hesitates to single out expeditions or individuals. Every degree of human strength, weakness, wisdom or folly was to play its part until in an ironical fashion, with the prize at hand, this age was to reach an apogee of profound and dramatic tragedy.

Today, as one reads back through the famous narratives of Ross, Parry, Franklin, Richardson and Back, one is again and again confronted with formidable tables of meteorological data, soundings, lists of plants, insects, birds, fish, lichens and always another beautifully engraved line on the map, another cape, another bay, another inlet; collecting, collecting, collecting, not only bringing piece-meal the physical environment of the North back to the Admiralty and thence to the Royal Society, but in the process lugging the bulky and rigid environment of the Admiralty and Royal Society to the Arctic.   Unable to duplicate, or ignoring, the lessons of the fur-trader explorers Dease and Simpson, with their genius for speed and adaptation, sooner or later this literal translation of what man in his new-found, scientific logic conceived as ultimate was bound to destroy him in the face of the remarkably illogical behaviour of the far North itself.

The grand and dreadful climax was reached accompanied by all the overtones and even the geographic backdrop which the most exacting playwright might conceive: the disaster of the third Franklin expedition in 1845-8: the total disappearance of its 129 men.   Twelve years of frenetic search followed.   At first, dedicated to possible rescue, it then became determination to know what had happened. Some thirty-eight individual and collective enterprises involving every sea, land, ice and snow transportation technique then known to science, the naval arts, the practical wisdom of fur-trader and native was utilized by one or the other of them with a successful blending of the latter in Rae and a sharing of the former in McClintock finally solving the riddle. In many ways this fatal gesture of man against the Arctic was to establish a stereotype and picture, to give substance to a great, popular nightmare which explorers themselves had bit by bit projected.   It had every element out of which whole mass illusions are created: an experienced, peerless leader, the confidence and might of a great and at times arrogant officialdom, the best that science could provide, and then: the goal within grasp, mystery, disappearance, ice, cold, the long arctic night, silence, desperate men, starvation, fearful natives, the struggle: now a few fragments, rumours of cannibalism, the ultimate sacrifice to the great dream, even the names of the ships themselves, H.M.S. *Erebus*, H.M.S. *Terror*.

With the closing of the drama in 1859, once again a new phase commences. This too, reflects far greater drives and interests than the locale suggests. Again, as in all the previous transitions, remnants of the preceding period still persist as the focus alters. The industrial age asserts itself in the increased change-over to steam. Growing competitive nationalisms, in prestige, if no longer in imperialism, are mirrored in the international race for the pole as into the Polar Basin press the flags of the United States, Norway as well as Britain and finally the emergence of Canada itself as sponsor in its own right of exploration. It is within this chronological framework that one finds the manifold expressions of civilization, ultimately sedentary, essentially restraining, fastening upon a fluctuating environment and a nomadic people—missionaries, the police. This was the era of the first, great geological surveys with economic utilization their hope and the intelligent blending of proven indigenous travel methods their instrument. Dawson and McConnell in the Yukon, and Dawson also in northern British Columbia, Tyrrell across the Barrens, Low in the Labrador Peninsula—in their admirable integrity, they paid meticulous credit to their fur-trader precursors, McLeod, Campbell, Hearne, Hendry, and McLean while bringing to their country the basic information from which its strength and wealth is even now but beginning to be tapped.

It is near the close of this 19th century and the opening of the new that one glimpses a curious contributing figure, the lone rebel to the urban, industrial age of utilization, the sportsman-explorer such as Whitney, Pike or Hanbury paradoxically hastening the very thing against which he is in revolt. In different category, but significant too, was the pioneer precision and efficiency of Douglas or the expression of independent theory, leading back to the ice-hunting stratum of antiquity itself, in Stefansson. The old dream, too, was laid to rest with Amundsen (1903-6) actually sailing the Northwest Passage in the *Gjoa*.

Since 1918, the patterns again emerge consonant with the larger cultural forms of the western world of which the far north is but a microcosm. Preeminently now are utilization and mechanical adaptation and all the shifting, varied constellations of a relativistic rather than finite and limited scientific concept. Today the helicopter hovers over Hearne's vanished footsteps. The vitamin replaces the whitefish, tri-metragon photography the straining eye. The Rorschach Test and psychoanalysis are creeping north to supplant the notebook of a Dr. Richardson or an Abbé Petitot. Caribou become desirable for their zygotic parasites rather than their possibility of pemmican. The simple distinctions of "primitive" and limestone rocks have become subject to the diamond drill, gravity anomalies and unbelievably complicated structural petrology. The very atmosphere itself, a century ago so carefully catalogued for its snow crystals, its simple refractions, its sundogs and the play of the aurora, is now tapped for microscopic specks of pollen and sub-microscopic cosmic rays. This is the nature of things. The mysteries will always be there. It is simply within the limits of the searcher's knowledge that exploration of the north may ever end.

One cannot leave this fragmental glimpse of the great quest without a lingering speculation as to what manner of men were these. For in all this pageant, something within himself draws forth the explorer from those who stay behind. Through the enormous record there are surprisingly few hints other than the most obvious and possibly least vital. It is as if there was a realization that the vastness of the natural world was too overpowering, too humbling to countenance the projection of the personal inner being. Yet, to him who seeks, there are glimpses; for these were and are men each living out his destiny as only he could so do. The almost mystical religiosity of Captain James, the mercurial, wonderful egotism of Radisson, the dogged faithfulness to duty of Hearne, the truly global dreams of Pond, the grasp of economic structure of Mackenzie, the rigidity to naval tradition of Franklin, the fractious petulance of McLean, the buoyant *elan* of Hanbury, the self-effacing integrity of Tyrrell, the calm assurance of todays' flying personnel, all of this and much more awaits the re-living and reinterpretation of Canadians for generations to come. The far north is there—waiting. The record is here to read. It is still to be finished, the exploration of the future, the discovery of the past.

What drew them onward? All the desires, wishes, hopes, despairs that men share with each other and with their time. Their reward? To some it was fame, to others oblivion, to all the quiet satisfaction of a challenge overcome, and to a few, perhaps, the realization of the words of the Eskimo, Igjugarjuk:

"All true wisdom is to be found far from the dwellings of men. . . ."

*J. Lewis Robinson, M.A., Ph.D., is chairman of the
geography division in the Department of Geology and
Geography at the University of British Columbia. He has
travelled widely in the North, and has written—by himself
or in collaboration with others—several books, pamphlets
and articles on the climate and geography of Canada.*

Northern Climate

by J. LEWIS ROBINSON

EVERYONE knows that northern Canada is cold. Every
schoolboy has heard of the long cold nights of the
arctic regions, and of the Eskimos who inhabit this chilly
wasteland. What is not generally known, however, is
that northern Canada is not cold everywhere, and that for
part of the year some sections can become very warm.
For most residents of North America it is also difficult to
compare this cold (or warmth) with that of other parts of
the world in similar latitudes.

There are many misconceptions about the climate of
northern Canada. It is hard to believe that much colder
temperatures are consistently experienced in the *subarctic*
areas of northern British Columbia or the northern Prairie
Provinces than have been recorded in arctic Canada. To
those who know of the arctic cold it is equally surprising
to hear of warm, shirtsleeve weather *north* of the Arctic
Circle in the Mackenzie River valley. To those who
visualize the Arctic as the Hollywood version of a Mountie
"mushing" through snow to his waist, it is news that most

of the Arctic has less precipitation than the dry belt of southern Alberta, and half the snowfall of any large eastern Canadian city.

One of the reasons for the confusion about the northern climate is that northern Canada covers a very large area. Yukon and Northwest Territories together total more than 1,500,000 square miles, which is about 40 percent of Canada. The areas of true arctic climate (which include northern Quebec) total about one million square miles, which is about 2½ times the size of the province of Ontario. In any such large area in the world there are bound to be differences in climate from place to place and variations from season to season.

Northern Canada has at least two distinct climates. In the northeast there is an arctic climate, while conditions in the northwestern areas are classed as subarctic. Climatologists have exact methods of defining an arctic climate, but in general it may be said that an arctic region is one where *the average mean temperature of the warmest month remains below 50° Fahrenheit*. This means that the warmest months of "summer" remain cool, since a 50° monthly average is similar to that experienced in Toronto in April or early November or in Vancouver in October. Nature has verified that the line which the climatologists have defined as the southern limit of the Arctic is a good one, for it coincides closely with the line marking the northern limit of trees. That is, the Arctic, because of its cool summers, is too cold for trees to grow.

This significant line which separates arctic and subarctic Canada is shown on the accompanying map. In general, the line extends from near the mouth of the Mackenzie River towards the southeast, appearing at Hudson Bay near Churchill, Manitoba. The arctic region also includes much of northwestern Quebec. In the Hudson Bay region the arctic climate is therefore more than 500 miles *south* of the Arctic Circle—the latter being a frequently misused mathematical line which has nothing to do directly with climate.

The climate of northwestern Canada, on the other hand, is called subarctic because the summers there become warm, and one to three months have averages *above* 50 degrees. This essential difference in climate means that the river valleys of the northwest have a good forest cover, there are agricultural possibilities, and life can be warm and pleasant during the summer. The difference in climate shows itself in the increasing population and the wider variety of resource developments in the northwest, whereas white penetration of the Eskimo territory of the northeast has proceeded very slowly and with notable difficulty.

The warm summers of the Yukon and Mackenzie valleys have frequently been attributed to the long duration of daylight in these regions during summer. It is true that during June and July there are from 18 to 24 hours of continuous daylight, and undoubtedly this sunlight, although coming in from low on the horizon, does help to raise temperatures, and gives a longer daily period of growth to garden crops. We know, however, that the number of hours of daylight is determined simply by the latitude of any place, and that all places in the same latitude have the same hours of daylight on the same days. If we then look at a map of Canada we see that southern Baffin Island and northeastern Keewatin District are in the same latitude as the warm areas of the Mackenzie valley. Since these areas are *not* warm in summer, and yet have the same long hours of daylight, there must be some other explanation of the difference in climate between northwestern and northeastern Canada.

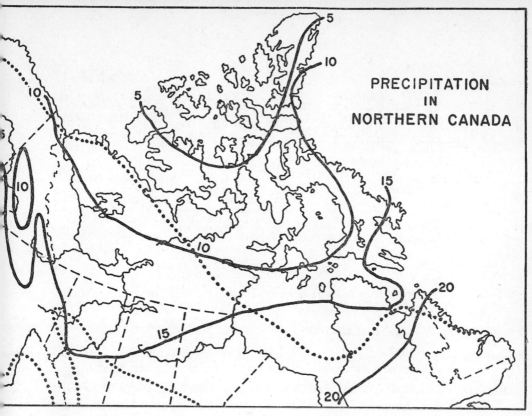

PRECIPITATION
IN
NORTHERN CANADA

The upper and lower dotted lines show the boundaries of the Arctic and Subarctic

One of the major differences in the geography of north-western and northeastern Canada is that the former is a large land mass, whereas the latter is an island and sea region. Most schoolboys have performed the experiment which shows that earth (or land) heats up more rapidly than does water, and gives off its heat more rapidly. On a large scale, therefore, the vast land area of northwestern Canada has the physical capacity of absorbing heat faster, and becomes warm in the summer. Conversely, it can become very cold in winter.

In addition, the islands and coasts of northeastern Can-ada are surrounded by cold water. The cold, ice-covered waters of the Arctic Ocean basin escape southward into the northwestern Atlantic Ocean, and one of the routes of movement is through the Canadian arctic islands. Water (and ice) moves, in general, from the north and west towards the south and east. Although this cold water is moving into southerly latitudes it warms very little in summer because during the period of longest daylight (June and July), the surface of the water is still largely ice-covered.

Thus Hudson Bay in summer is a large body of cold water, which, in turn, chills the lands around it and has a major influence over the climate of eastern and northeastern Canada. Chiefly due to this large indentation of water, the less desirable arctic climate is extended far southward and removes a large area of Canada from the possibility of forest or agricultural development.

One further contrast might be noted to show the dominant influence of cold waters on climate and the resultant economic development. One has but to compare the east coast of Baffin Island and the west coast of Greenland, on opposite sides of Davis Strait, and in the same latitude. Baffin Island, with a southward-moving cold current along shore, has a barren, bleak coast with few people and few possible resources or occupations. Southwestern Greenland, in contrast, with a warmer northward current or upwelling, has a sheep-grazing industry, local gardens, and a prosperous cod-fishing industry. Although undoubtedly other human factors have had an influence in this contrast, the dominant control has been that of climate.

It is no surprise to know that northern Canada is severely cold in winter, but this cold does not have the same intensity throughout the large area. In considering the "cold" of a region one has to differentiate between extremes —which occur only occasionally, but are much talked about —and the monthly averages, which give a more accurate, long-term picture of the climate. A comparison of the average monthly temperatures shows that the coldest part of Canada in mid-winter (January) is the group of far-

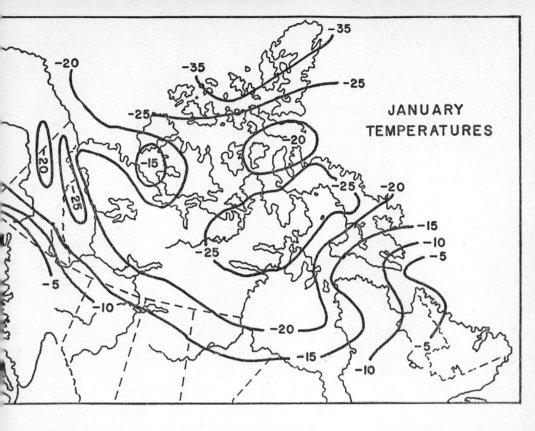

JANUARY
TEMPERATURES

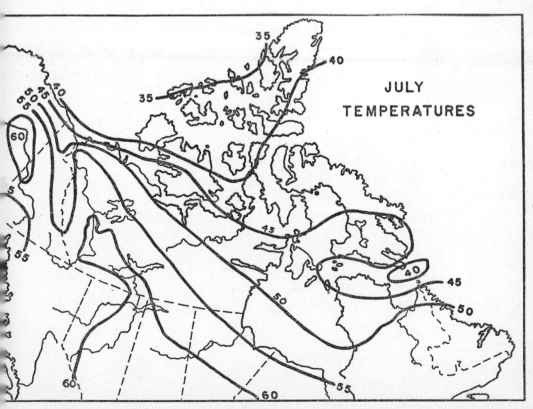

JULY
TEMPERATURES

northern arctic islands where weather stations only recently
have been established.   Although the extreme cold noted
there has not been excessive, the averages remain very low
(about 35° below zero for the month), because there are
about three months of the winter when the sun is below
the horizon and no solar heat is received.

The second coldest part of Canada is the vast, almost
unoccupied area, northwest of Hudson Bay.   In this region
of northern Keewatin district average monthly temperatures
are about 25° below zero.   Although this is surely considered cold, we have but to compare this average with
temperatures in northeastern Siberia, to realize the "moder-
ating" effect of the cold water of Hudson Bay and adjoining
straits in winter.   In the vast, cold landmass of northeastern Siberia the average monthly mean temperature is
about -60°, and extremes of -90° to -100° have been verified.
It is thus apparent that cold, ice-covered water does not
cool off as much as cold land.

Most of the rest of northern Canada has monthly average temperatures of about -15° to -20°, except for a "mild"
area near the entrance to Hudson Strait.   The weather
station there at Resolution Island has a January average
temperature of about zero degrees, which is slightly higher
than the January average for Winnipeg, about 800 miles
farther south.

Although of less practical value, the figures recording
extreme temperatures are usually more interesting because
they tell one just how cold a place can become.   The Arctic,
because much of its area is ice over water in winter, does not
become as cold as places in the landmass of northwestern
Canada.   The lowest temperature yet recorded in the
Canadian Arctic is 63° below zero.   Most Canadians will
recognize that much lower temperatures are known in the
Mackenzie valley, Yukon, and the northern Prairie Pro-

vinces. For example, the "cold pole" of North America
used to be the -79° recorded at Fort Good Hope, on the
Mackenzie River. However, the new record low, set in
1947, was noted at Snag, in western Yukon, with 81° below.
Although the extremes have become colder, the annual
averages in the North are becoming warmer. This "warming" influence in northern winters has been quite noticeable
since about 1920, and is shown in the rapid way that glaciers
have been retreating and sea-ice conditions have become less
serious.

Fortunately, northern Canada is not always a land of
severe cold. As the daylight period lengthens after March,
the snow begins to melt, and the ice of the mainland rivers
and lakes begins to soften. By late May most of the snow
has disappeared from the Mackenzie valley, and during
June the southern parts of the arctic areas become snow-free.
The ice cover of the lakes of mainland Canada begins to
break up during June and early July, depending upon the
size and depth of the lakes. Throughout July the sea-ice
off the mainland loosens from the shore and drifts around
with the ocean currents or is pushed about by winds. To
the northward solid ice may still be found across some of
the straits and channels in early August, and it is likely that
the ice joining the northwestern group of islands (Borden,
Ringnes, and others) never breaks up during summer.

During the summer months the valleys in the landmass
of northwestern Canada heat up. This warming is assisted
by movement into the region of relatively warm air masses
from the Pacific Ocean or from the prairies. Average
monthly temperatures in July around Dawson, Y.T., and
in the southern Mackenzie River valley, are about 60
degrees. This warmth is the same average as that recorded
in the Clay Belt of Ontario and across the central Prairie
Provinces to the Peace River area. In addition, however,

the period of daylight is much longer in the Northwest
Territories and Yukon.   Since it is recognized that the Clay
Belt and Peace River are now established agricultural
regions, it is apparent that average summer temperatures are
no deterrent to the northward expansion of Canadian
agriculture.

Not only are monthly summer averages warm in northwestern Canada, but the record of extreme temperatures
shows that it can become very hot.   Fort Smith, on the
southern boundary of the Northwest Territories, once
officially recorded 103°—which is hotter than has ever
been recorded in Windsor, Ontario, Canada's most southerly city!   All weather stations in the Mackenzie valley, and
Dawson in the Yukon, have noted extremes of over 90
degrees at some time in their recent history, and extremes
above 80 degrees are frequent every summer.   Thus it
used to be possible for summer visitors to go down the
Mackenzie valley and cross the Arctic Circle near Fort Good
Hope in shirt sleeves with temperatures sweltering near 80
degrees.   If these visitors used the Arctic Circle as their
definition of the arctic region, they certainly were receiving
the wrong impression of the true Arctic.

Northeastern, or arctic Canada, is distinct climatically
in that it has no "summer" months, as a climatologist
defines them.   Average monthly temperatures remain
below 50°, and in the northern arctic islands, the average
for the warmest month may be only about 35°.   As was
noted earlier, temperatures are kept low by the cold water
and melting ice around the islands, but also because warm
air masses from southern or western Canada seldom are able
to penetrate far into the region.

Although monthly averages remain below 50°, there are
many days in July and August when afternoon temperatures rise into the pleasant 60's.   At all weather stations

there are records of temperature as high as 75 degrees, and at a few stations there have been hot days of over 80 degrees. These official recordings show that there are times when the Arctic can be a pleasant, warm place, with colourful flowers blooming over the tundra, and a clear blue sky above. However, too frequently the temperature of a "summer" day is in the cool 50's, low grey clouds fill the sky, and the high humidity penetrates one's field clothing.

Even in the arctic regions of northeastern Canada there is a short time of the year when temperatures remain above the frost point of 32°. The mission gardens at Chesterfield Inlet have an average frost-free season of about 65 days, which is equal to the average period without frost experienced at Vanderhoof in the agricultural area of central B.C. The latter, however, receives more heat during the summer season. Likewise, the frost-free season of about 50 days at Port Harrison, on the east side of Hudson Bay, is longer than that recorded between Oba and Long Lac, along the C.N.R. in the western part of the Ontario Clay Belt.

The characteristic picture of northern Canada as a land of deep snows and ice is hard to dispel. It is true that there is a long period during the year when the region is under snow-cover, but snow never accumulates to depths like those known in southeastern Canada or northeastern United States. In the settled river valleys of the Yukon and Mackenzie District the annual precipitation is from 10 to 13 inches. This is the same as that recorded in the dry areas of southeastern Alberta and the southern interior of British Columbia, and is about one-third of that which falls upon Toronto. About half of the total precipitation in northwestern Canada is snowfall which begins to settle upon the land in October. Although the Canadian Meteorological Service uses the official conversion figure of 10 inches of snow to equal 1 inch of water, it is recognized in the Arctic that the hard, granular snow of the north is much less "wet" than that known in southern Canada.

The above figures indicate that one of the problems of agriculture in the North is the small amount of summer rainfall. Since only about five inches of rain come during the four summer months (about four inches in *one* month is the usual amount expected at Halifax in the summer), drought is to be feared almost as much as an unseasonable early frost in the northwestern valleys.

All of the Arctic Islands, except southeastern Baffin Island, record less than ten inches of annual precipitation. Since ten inches is the figure often used by geographers to delimit a desert area, it is apparent that the Arctic can be classed as one of the cold deserts of the world. Since the Arctic region has temperatures above 32° for a few months of the summer, it should be apparent that the region is snow-free for that time, and that the small amount of precipitation falls then as rain. The amount of annual precipitation decreases to the northward across the arctic islands, because the source of moisture—air masses from the Arctic Ocean—contains very little water-vapour, and there are no mountains in the western islands to cause the air to drop its small load. The central islands record less than five inches annually, and the new weather stations in the far northern islands have recorded only two or three inches in a year. These latter stations are, therefore, by far the driest in Canada (by comparison, Medicine Hat, Alberta, has 11 inches annually), and can be compared with the two inches that is recorded in the desert at Cairo in Egypt.

Although there is little precipitation in the North, cloud cover is quite characteristic. Clouds are common in the winter, when the earth cools off during the long nights, but they are much more of a problem during the summer. Over the arctic islands summer cloud cover is almost consistent, as cold air over the arctic waters mixes with slightly warmer air over the land. This problem is one of the most serious encountered by airplanes which attempt to move about from island to island. In the same way, the summer is the worst time for fogs along the arctic coasts. Resolution Island, at the eastern entrance to Hudson Strait, has an average of fifteen days of fog during the month of July. The hazards of navigation are therefore increased both in the air and on the sea by the cloudy character of the arctic climate.

Our northern climate is frequently misunderstood and maligned. Too often one hears downright statements made about the North as a whole which apply only to certain parts of it. We have noted that there are distinct differ-ences in climate between northwestern and northeastern Canada. If one appreciates these differences it is much easier to understand some of the problems of resource development and human adaptations as they vary from place to place across our northern lands.

Much of what one does in the north is related to or influenced by the climate. Since we cannot change the climate, at least we can try to understand it and work with it. Nature is helping in a small way by reducing the intensity of the winter cold, but for the next few decades at least future development of the North will have to penetrate into a region which will be climatically little changed. The climate offers many barriers, but it also suggests some hopeful possibilities. In order to use the possibilities and avoid the difficulties we first must know more about the climatic facts.

Douglas Leechman, B.Sc., M.A., Ph.D., F.R.S.C., is the senior anthropologist at the National Museum in Ottawa. A prolific writer and lecturer, he is the author of—among other books—"Eskimo Summer" and "Indian Summer." He has travelled widely from coast to coast among the native peoples of Canada, studying and recording their past and present ways of life.

Men of the Woodlands

by DOUGLAS LEECHMAN

ALL the Indians living north of 55°, with a few minor exceptions, speak languages of two linguistic stocks, the Algonkian and the Athapascan. The exceptions are the Tsimshian who live on the Nass and Skeena Rivers in British Columbia, and the Tlinkit of the southern interior of the Yukon. To the north are the Eskimo, who are discussed in another chapter.

The Algonkian-speaking people consist of a few small bands of Naskapi-Montagnais in the northern interior of Quebec and those Cree who live to the south of the Churchill River in Saskatchewan, Manitoba and Ontario. The Athapascan people occupy a much greater area than these, extending from the Yukon and northern British Columbia eastwards to the limit of trees and the barren lands. Several tribes may be distinguished, the Kutchin and Tahltan in the west, the Hare, Dogrib, Nahani, Slave, Sekani, and Beaver in the drainage basin of the Mackenzie River, the Yellow-knives and Chipewyan farther to the east. With but minor differences, imposed by variations in conditions, all these people, from northern Quebec to the Yukon, follow a very similar mode of existence, depending on the forests and lakes, the tundra and the rivers, for their food and shelter, and what may be said of one group can, with modifications, be attributed to them all.

The population today is not large. It probably never was, for this is anything but a fertile country and could never support more than a few bands of wandering hunters and trappers. There are perhaps ten thousand Atha-pascans in the area and only a few hundred Crees and Montagnais. They all show the Mongoloid characteristics typical of the North American Indian: straight, black hair; high cheek bones; copper-coloured skin; dark brown eyes; and a tendency—more easily observed in the women and children perhaps—to the Mongolian eye. They are fairly tall and well built, in contrast to the shorter and heavier Eskimo and West Coast Indians.

Their social organization, even before the coming of the whites, used to be rudimentary in the extreme. They had no chiefs, as we understand the term, and even their division into separate tribes was based on differences in dialect rather than on any social distinction. Usually the separate wandering bands, linked together by marriage or con-venience, recognized only the leadership of the man whose stronger personality assured him such a position, and even he was seldom able to enforce his wishes against the will of other members of the band. Social groups, called phratries, were recognized in some tribes, and marriage outside the phratry was obligatory, but this system is rapidly breaking down under the impact of the advancing white culture.

Not only is the weak social organization crumbling, but so too are the old ways of life.   In many parts of northern Canada hunting and trapping is no longer remunerative and the people have had to turn to new ways of making a living. The techniques of hunting and fishing were, at one time, highly specialized, varying with the kind of game being pursued and the season of the year.   The musk-ox, which has the habit of standing when attacked, forming a tight semi-circle, was held at bay with dogs and shot down with a bow.   The moose, a solitary animal which does not stand at bay unless cornered, was usually taken in strong babiche snares or shot with the bow.   Caribou might be snared or shot, and many were taken by spearing them from canoes as they crossed a river or lake.   Most other large animals, even bears, were taken in snares, and these are still used extensively.   Beaver were taken in nets in the old days, and fish too were netted.   The inner bark of the willow provides a reasonably tough fibre which was used for fish nets.   The labour involved was considerable, and much of the work of twisting the fibres and the actual netting had to be done under water to keep the fibre pliable.

The meat and fish obtained in these various ways made up the principal food supplies, and any other game obtainable, such as ducks and grouse, was added.   Berries, roots of a few kinds, the soft inner bark of some trees, and tender green shoots plucked in spring, were almost the only vegetable items in their diet.   Pemmican was made in much the same way as it was on the prairies, sometimes with the addition of berries, and both meat and fish was used for this purpose.   Other meat was cut into thin slices and dried to preserve it for use in the winter.   Fresh meat was cooked by boiling.   No pottery vessels were available, so the food to be cooked was put in birch bark vessels with water, and hot stones were used to bring it to a boil.   While by no means as efficient as boiling in vessels which could be put right on the fire, the stone boiling method was nevertheless effective and was very widely used.

Food was never abundant, or rarely so, and all too often it was lacking. Starvation was always a possibility and a bad season or a run of poor luck could reduce even the most skilful hunter to want. Various emergency foods were used, such as *tripe de roche*, but there are many cases known in the North of families so desperately short of food as to be reduced to cannibalism. Even today, people remote from a trading post may find themselves threatened by starvation.

Their semi-nomadic life made the construction of permanent houses impracticable. Variants of the "wig-wam" were common, consisting of a shelter made by cover-ing a structure of poles with sheets of bark or hides or a thatch of the branches of coniferous trees. The degree of care with which these were built depended on how long they were to be used and the severity of the weather. In winter, especially in the west, a favourite dwelling consisted of two open tents which faced each other a few feet apart with a fire built between them. This heated both tents, afforded easy access, and allowed the smoke to escape readily. Now that the white trapper and prospector have invaded the north, many Indians have copied their log cabins, dwellings which are easily built from local materials and which are easy to keep warm in winter.

In such temporary homes, and labouring under the necessity of moving all possessions each time camp was struck, there was a natural tendency to cut down the furni-ture and tools to the barest minimum. Beds were of hides on spruce boughs, which can be very comfortable if properly laid. Bowls and spoons were whittled from wood, and arrowheads, knives, and skin scrapers were chipped from fine-grained stone. The Yellowknives found deposits of copper nuggets in their country, as did some of the southern Kutchin, and made a variety of tools by hammering out this malleable metal. Men had also stone hammers and adzes, and the women made awls and needles of bone.

Clothing posed almost as big a problem for these people as it did for the Eskimo. It had to be made of readily available material, proof against hard usage, and warm enough to withstand very low temperatures. The only material which fulfilled all these requirements was the skins of animals, either dehaired or dressed with the fur on. Moose, caribou, and deer hides were all used, especially the two first, and smaller furs such as beaver and muskrat were used for trimming and other minor purposes. The usual garments were a tunic or shirt which, in the case of men, fell a little below the top of the long leggings. For women the tunic was longer. Moccasins might be separate or attached to the leggings. Clothing was often decorated with paint, usually red, and an embroidery of porcupine quills or, in post-European days, beads. In winter, when extra warmth was needed, a robe of skins was worn in addition to the tunic and leggings. This robe might be of ground squirrel or ground hog skins, or of beaver. It was not usual to wear a hat, but in winter a skin was sometimes worn on the head. Today most of the Indians dress in white man's clothes, rather shabby in appearance and with only the moccasins and sometimes a deerskin shirt retained from their native costume.

Travel in winter was a good deal easier than in the summer, for the lakes, swamps, and streams were all frozen and even the large rivers could be crossed on the ice at many points. Snow blanketed the ground and toboggans could be used for transporting the heavier loads. Smaller loads were carried by the women, who also pulled the toboggans, and dogs were also pressed into service as pack animals. Snowshoes were in almost universal use here, generally a long narrow shoe with the toe turned sharply up, in marked contrast to the round bear-paw snowshoe of the east.

In summer, travel was by canoe but not as extensively as in Ontario and Quebec. Birch bark and spruce bark were both used, and another type of canoe made by covering a wooden framework with hides that had been scraped thin and then sewn together. These were used principally for trips down river and, once the journey was accomplished, the hides were salvaged and the frame discarded.

Children were carried in bags of skin, with a packing of moss. Cradles of various types were used here and there, and today many women carry their children under the shawl, with a belt to support the child's seat.

Life was generally difficult. Hunting and fishing took up most of the time and any mental picture of a happy and lazy life in the woods is far from accurate. There was little in the way of social intercourse, for the small bands of people came in contact with each other only at intervals, each family living to itself. There might be a small gathering and a feast on the occasion of a death, or of the chance meeting of a few groups together. On many of these occasions the men wrestled with each other, the prize being the wife of the vanquished, who stood stolidly by while her fate was being decided. Men who were able hunters often had more than one wife, frequently sisters for they were thought to quarrel less than women who were not intimately connected. The women especially endured a hard life, with endless tasks of cooking, caring for the children and the home, and the eternal scraping and preparation of skins. Not infrequently female babies were allowed to die, for their mothers thought that this was a kinder fate than the one they would suffer if they lived.

Dogs were the only domestic animals, though occasionally a young or injured wild animal might be kept as a pet.
The dogs were used for packing rather than for pulling
sleds or toboggans as they are today.   At least two aboriginal breeds are known, both of them having presumably
been brought in the first place from the Old World.   The
larger kind were those used for packing, but in the Yukon
and northern British Columbia, a smaller breed, the Hare or
Tahltan Bear Dog, is still to be found.   They are about the
size of a large fox terrier, black and white with a curled tail,
and make friendly and affectionate pets.   They were used
in small packs, being trained to tree a bear and hold it till
the hunter came.

Gambling was a favourite recreation when a group of
men got together, one of the most common games being the
"hand game," resembling our game of "Hide the Button."
Drumming and chanting, and a lot of hand movements
designed to mislead the opponents, were all part of the game
and large stakes were often wagered, even to several years of
servitude, or the sacrifice of one's women.   Dancing was
popular, and the children used to vie with each other in
wrestling, racing, and archery.

Music was confined to singing, with a drum as accom-
paniment.   The drum was of the single-headed tambourine
type.   Songs were of various kinds, lullabies, love songs,
weather incantations, and dance songs.   The people had
also a host of legends and myths and most of the older
women had large repertoires.   Tale telling was confined to
the winter, when the short hours of daylight kept the
people huddled round the camp fire with little to do in the
evenings but eat, talk, and sleep.

The arts were but poorly developed, as one might
imagine.   Some clothing as has been said was decorated
with porcupine quill work or with paint, and the only

elaborate art form known was practised in the valley of the Mackenzie River where dyed porcupine quills were woven into a web of sinew in intricate and singularly beautiful patterns. These were used as trimming for clothing and baby-carrying straps and, in later years, as hat bands and on gun coats. The art is dying out and aniline dyes have taken the place of the older vegetable dyes in the few examples that are still made.

Spiritual affairs were in the hands of the medicine men, who served as doctors, priests, and magicians. Medicine came within the realm of spiritual affairs, for sickness was thought to be caused more often by witchcraft than by natural causes. If a man fell and broke his leg, it was because a spell had been laid upon him by an enemy, and the duty of the medicine man was to find the enemy and counteract his influence by the use of an even stronger charm. Simple surgery, such as the lancing of a boil or the setting of a broken leg, was undertaken, but curing generally consisted in chanting and drumming, with a lot of blowing on the patient's body and the sucking out of it of bits of stone or wood that the medicine man had previously concealed somewhere about his person.

As magicians, the medicine men performed simple conjuring tricks and essayed to foretell the future. This they could do, they said, because of their intimacy with spiritual familiars. The forests and streams were thought to be populated by large numbers of spirits, some of them dangerous to mankind, but most of them indifferent. The dangerous spirits had to be propitiated when necessary, which was usually done by muttering some talismanic phrase or making a small offering of food or tobacco. As in most parts of the sub-polar regions, when a bear was killed, songs of explanation and apology were sung and the body was treated with ceremony and respect.

As a rule, the dead were cremated, or bodies might be wrapped in a hide and placed high up in a tree. At other times, the dead were laid on the ground and covered by a cairn of stones, much as was done by the Eskimo. Frequently the dead man's clothes and other personal possessions were burned, but some of the more valuable objects might be distributed among his survivors.

So far we have considered the Indians of this huge sub-continent as they were before the culture of the white man had produced much effect on them, but conditions today are by no means what they were a hundred, or even fifty, years ago. In the beginning, not only did the introduction of new tools, new weapons, and new foods render many of the old native crafts obsolete so that they were soon forgotten, but the frequent marriage of the fur trader with a native woman, whether with or without benefit of clergy, hastened the acceptance of higher standards of conduct, better methods of cooking, and even in some cases broader fields of thought.

In recent years, the change that had already so strongly affected the native culture has moved more rapidly. New means of transportation, especially the aeroplane and modern highways, the impact of the Second Great War on the North, and the recent impetus given to mining, have all led to an increase in the number of white men in the Northwest Territories and a steady reduction in the fur, game, and fish on which the natives, as well as the old timers among the white residents, depended so largely. Now, the old way of life is no longer possible. The fur is trapped out, the game is hunted out, the rivers and lakes are fished out. Not entirely, of course, but in many places to such an extent as to make depending on them for food no longer practicable.

Game, never abundant except for the vast herds of caribou, is now scarce almost everywhere and in a good many areas it is almost non-existent. One man was heard to say that he had seen more big game in New York State than he ever had in the Northwest Territories, and his statement is completely credible.

Once widely scattered, there has been a continuous tendency for the Indians to congregate about the fur trading posts, clotted together in little settlements of their own. Here many of them live in reasonably comfortable, but not particularly sanitary, log cabins, often moving into tents for the summer. A good many of them have little gardens in which they grow potatoes, lettuce, and radishes. There is no farming, except by a few white enthusiasts at the missions and other posts. There are practically no cattle or horses owned by the Indians north of 55°. Many of them, Indians, half-breeds, and Indian women married to whites, still dry fish and wild berries for the winter, which is an excellent thing and much to be encouraged, for these natural foods are a good deal more nutritious than many of the commercially prepared foods available at the posts.

The men accept what work they can get. Some are engaged in commercial fishing or lumbering, others find work as guides, packers, canoe men, or as casual laborers. Few of them work for themselves, rather than for wages. Wherever it is profitable, many men still run their trap lines in winter and make substantial sums from this occupation, which can be carried on when the summer activities of mining and transportation have shut down.

The Indians are not confined to reservations as they are in the more densely populated south of Canada, and they earnestly hope that they never will be. They are by no means neglected, however, for they are under the direct care and supervision of the Indian Affairs Branch of the

Department of Citizenship and Immigration. Every year sees an increase in the money and effort devoted to their betterment, and the government officials in charge of this work have shown commendable energy and great ability in the last few years, watching for every opportunity of improving the conditions under which these Indians live.

The present policy is to see that the Indians receive all the benefits that other Canadian citizens are entitled to, so they are now paid Family Allowances (in kind rather than in money), Old Age Pensions, Pensions for the Blind, and relief for needy or incapacitated individuals. This in addition to the small annual payments of treaty money which most of them receive. Family Allowances have been most heartily welcomed by the Indians and every addition to the family is hailed with great enthusiasm.

Game reserves and sanctuaries have been established in which only natives may hunt or trap. By this means, not only have Indians who might otherwise have found game difficult to obtain been assisted, but the game is allowed to live a comparatively undisturbed life, to its great benefit, and surplus animals spread beyond the boundaries of the reserves to increase the general supply. Over 160,000 square miles have been so reserved in various parts of the Northwest Territories and a much larger area in the Arctic Islands.

Recently there have been improvements in the schools available to the natives. The tendency now is to establish non-denominational day schools, some of them attended by both white and Indian children, under the care of well-qualified teachers, trained in modern methods, who also act as social welfare workers in the Indian community in which they are stationed. Films, radio, new supplies and a new enthusiasm have brought obvious success to the first, somewhat tentative, experiments.

The first decades of white contact saw the Indians seriously affected by diseases which, up to that time, had been only sporadic, if known at all. The natives, seldom exposed to them, had built up no immunity and even a mild attack of some contagious disease might well result in death, and a small or large epidemic. Measles, smallpox, influenza, tuberculosis, and venereal diseases seem to have been the most dangerous.

Not only were contagious diseases (and alcohol) undermining the health of the native people, but a general malaise caused by unsuitable food and clothing did great damage too.

Medical care and hospitalization of the Indians is now under the supervision of the Indian Health Services of the Department of National Health and Welfare. They help the mission hospitals already established, maintain others of their own, and station fully qualified doctors and nurses in the North, always ready to give professional advice and assistance, either by radio or, if that seems to be insufficient, to visit a distant patient themselves without delay.

At one time, there was good reason to believe that the Indians were becoming extinct. The native population of the Northwest Territories had been reduced to about a third of what it once was, and the outlook for their survival was not encouraging. At about the beginning of this century conditions improved and the Indians showed an increase in numbers which has continued steadily for the past fifty years (about one percent per annum for Canada as a whole). With the reduction in infant mortality, better care of the aged, better food for children and adults, more financial assistance, and better schools, the future for the Indians of the Northwest Territories looks brighter than it has done for a long time.

Squadron Leader A. D. Copland, M.B.E. served the Arctic division of the Hudson's Bay Company for over 18 years, travelling extensively among the western and eastern Eskimos. In 1942 he joined the R.C.A.F., with whom he served in the Eastern Arctic. In 1949 he was seconded to the Arctic research section of the Defence Research Board in Ottawa, and he is now back with the Air Force developing equipment for cold weather areas.

Men of the Barrens

by A. D. COPLAND

ANYBODY who visits the Arctic for the first time must wonder why, of all the vast spaces of the north, the Eskimos chose this cold and barren land to live in. During the brief, cool summer almost nothing grows there but a few flowers, stunted willows and moss where conditions are favourable. In the long, bitter winter months, when gales howl out of the north, the drifting snow blankets the land and frozen sea, and for weeks—or even months—at a time, the sun sinks below the horizon and darkness spreads like a pall over the lifeless scene.

Yet the Eskimo loves his land; he is amongst the most cheerful of human beings and, strange as it may seem, it is in the harsh winter, not the softer summer, that he comes into his own.

The fact is, that for centuries of living in this inhospitable land, the Eskimo has developed a way of life entirely suited to his environment, and one that has brought forth all his admirable qualities—strength and stamina, resourcefulness and initiative, cheerfulness, generosity and courage.

Primarily the Eskimo is a nomad hunter, and almost all his skill has been directed towards the pursuit of animals for food. In perfecting the weapons and implements of the chase, his natural genius for simple mechanics comes to the fore—in the construction of the "breakdown" harpoon; the throwing stick to give greater distance to the many-barbed bird spear; the strong but resilient sled with its iced runners; and that ideal shelter for the arctic nomad, the spiral-domed snowhouse.

If the seal and the caribou were to return to their former abundance, the Eskimo could still live happily and independently off the land. The seal is to the sea-coast Eskimo what the caribou is to the inland native—his staff of life. The seal provides him with food for his family and his dogs; with summer clothing and shelter material; with skins for his kayak; with warmth, light and a multiplicity of useful articles such as harpoon lines and floats, sled lashings, dog harness and traces, and whip lashes. The caribou provides a similar bounty for the inland native, except that the lack of fuel is offset by the excellent clothing and bedding which is more suited for winter than summer.

All year round the Eskimo hunter is in active pursuit of life's necessities for his family. Sealskins are at their best in the fall, the meat is excellent and the animals float easily from the heavy covering of fat beneath the skin. Under the powerful sweep of the double bladed paddle the graceful sealskin kayaks skim over the surface of the water. Harpoons are ready on the narrow decks, and attached to each by a sealskin line is an *avatak* or sealskin bladder which marks the position of a speared seal while under water and prevents possible loss through sinking. With the paddle used as an outrigger to stabilize the craft, the hunter skins and cuts up the seal in the water, then stows the meat fore and aft in his kayak.   And in the evening the heavily laden craft glide homeward under the slow strokes of the weary hunters, who are welcomed on the beaches by the women, the children and the dogs.

Walrus hunting in the late fall provides the excitement and risk dearly loved by the Eskimo.   Slowly the Peterhead boats glide down on the feeding herds.   Hunters man all quarters of the boat with gear in readiness and lines carefully coiled.   Several strikes may be made at the same time and then pandemonium breaks loose.   The sea is dotted by maddened walrus who may charge the boat at any time. Eagerly watching the dancing *avataks*, the hunters wait for the doomed animals to re-appear—which they usually do in a state of complete exhaustion from the hurried dive. High-powered rifles aimed at the one vulnerable spot behind the eardrum quickly end the struggle.

The carcasses are towed ashore hanging from the gun-wales of the boats and then the cutting up starts.   What a primitive sight that is!   Working in blood to the wrists, the hunters, with the remarkable skill that springs from their knowledge of anatomy, quickly dismember the huge beasts. When the portions are laid out in slabs of roughly two hundred pounds of hide, fat and meat, slots are cut around the edge of the hide through which are reeved strips of skin to draw everything into a compact bundle, which is then cached in the stone covered mound favoured by the Eskimo.

When the cold prevailing winter wind sweeps down across the wide, deep bays in the late fall, young ice quickly forms.   It is then that the bears haul out of the sea in prime condition for winter sleep.   For untold centuries Eskimo have killed bear, and this is still the crowning achievement. Dogs are trained from puppyhood in the art of bear-baiting, usually from first hand experience. It is indeed an impressive sight to see the lumbering beast at bay, legs wide apart, body crouched low while the great head swings, snaps and snarls at the dogs dancing around him. Bear are seldom dangerous to humans but occasionally people have had unfortunate encounters with old dog bears. These animals sometimes fail to get into condition for winter hibernation, due to impaired faculties, and wander around in winter searching for food.

Bear meat is rich and prized by the Eskimo, but great pains are taken to ensure that the liver is removed and buried deep in the ice where no animal will find it. Where bear liver has been eaten violent sickness usually follows. Recently scientists have confirmed the Eskimo belief, by proving that polar bear liver carries a remarkably heavy concentration of vitamin A.

The winter fox hunt is important to the Eskimo because the revenue derived from it provides all the things that their present circumstances require. In this field the natural talents of the Eskimo are well employed. It is unfortunate, however, that the prices paid for fox skins vary considerably from year to year in accordance with the state of the world market.

Fox trapping starts in November and the number of steel traps used by individuals varies from about fifty to several hundred. Early in the season quick returns are almost sure around the stone meat caches, but generally the trapline is laid out according to "signs" which the Eskimo know from long experience will give the best results. Frequently two men will share a trapline, and since the only equipment carried on the line is sleeping skins, rifles, snowknives and a piece of frozen meat, they can make good time. Small overnight igloos are built, within which, with arms withdrawn from the sleeves of their loose-fitting

garments, Eskimos trappers will spend a comfortable night
under conditions in which a white man would have difficulty
in sleeping at all.

The Eskimo indeed finds that trapping suits him admirably.   He is by nature a nomad, and for him, winter is
the time of travel.   Moreover, he has an amazing sense of
direction, even when all landmarks are completely obliter-
ated by drifting snow.   There are no regular trails in the
true sense of the word and the general direction of travel
frequently depends on the extent of the snow coverage.
During the winter the frozen sea and the rivers and lakes of
the interior become the highways.   The Eskimo is a de-
lightful travelling companion, and the monotony of long
hours in small snowhouses is made bearable by his cheerful
good humour and natural courtesy.

A dogteam is necessary to an Eskimo since it gives that
slow, certain means of travel which so well suits his tem-
perament and his needs.   The care of a team is a family
responsibility, and the young dogs are early in life given
that handling and roughing by the children that make them
manageable in later life.   The behaviour of sled dogs in
harness largely depends on the weather.   With a bitter
head wind and stinging ground-drift they pull steadily on
the rawhide traces, seldom needing any encouragement from
the driver.   But when conditions are pleasant they can
afford to indulge in frequent quarrels, each dog blaming his
neighbour for some imagined grievance until a general fight
starts.   Then the long, forty-foot lash whistles into the
melee and discipline is restored.

Early fall sees the dogs eager to be in harness and the
first hundred-yard dash is usually a wildly enthusiastic race.
But cold winter days find them cringing before the frozen
harness when the driver comes near to put it on.   In the
spring they usually slink away to nurse paws that may have

been injured by the sharp ice. Under these conditions sealskin dog boots are used with small holes for the claws to pass through.

The Eskimo plank sled or *kahmotik* is of relatively simple construction, the cross-bars being lashed to the runners with rawhide lines. While travelling over rough terrain or ice, there is considerable movement so that loads have to be securely lashed. The nose is built up to give the rise that will allow the sled to negotiate rolling snowdrifts, while the heel of the runners is tapered off to prevent drag and give greater manoeuverability in rough ground. Steel shoeing is used during the fall and spring, but in winter a fine-textured peat is prepared and frozen on the runners. This peat mud when frozen is planed smooth and the surface is then coated with ice.

The period of sled travel is extended well into spring, or even early summer, when the fast mounting sun and lengthening days set the tempo of the seal hunt. Behind white cotton shields, the hunters crawl up on the basking seals and shoot them at close range.

The seal harvest from the rotting spring ice is one of the important economic factors of Eskimo life. Oil and meat must be obtained now for winter use. Although skins at this time of the year are not good enough for clothing, the pelts are cleverly removed from the animal without cutting or mutilating them in any way. These sealskin pokes are filled with strips of fat which are rendered into oil by the heat of the sun. A reserve of meat, the traditional *nipkoo* of the Eskimo, is perfectly preserved in the brisk winds that dry it to perfection on the racks.

The transition to summer is rapid and impressive as the rushing rivers and turbulent mountain streams bring down an abundance of the splendid arctic char. Transformed by its annual visit to the salt water, in a matter of days the char is a virile fish with bright red undersides.* This seasonal abundance is not lost on the Eskimo. Nets are set out on the coast where they soon hang under the weight of the catch. Old river fish traps are again used. Into these circular stone traps called *sapootins* the fish are cleverly manoeuvered, the entrance is closed by a stone, and the Eskimo wade in to begin the slaughter with their *kakevuks* or three-pronged spears.

Fish is generally a seasonal food, or one that is sought in an emergency when the supply of meat runs out. In some parts of the Arctic it is dried, or stored in perennially frozen ground for use exclusively as dog food. So numerous are fish at certain seasons that community feasts of fish heads are common. Meat and fish are more often eaten raw than cooked, generally because it is not always convenient or possible to cook it, but mostly because it is a traditional custom to eat it in this manner.

The long, warm summer days bring a return to the sea, and white sails may be seen offshore where the men hunt seal and white whale. *Muktuk*, the outer skin of this whale is considered a delicacy. It tastes like shellfish and is really a protective covering for a fine leather which the traders salt down for export. Also at this season of the year the silver haired skins of the young harbour seal are prized for boot legs. This is a busy season for the women, since the skins from the early spring hunt have been processed into leather from which the remarkable sealskin boots are made. Sole leather from the *oogjuk* or bearded seal's skin is cut to shape and given to the old women and children for softening by chewing, which the Eskimo centuries ago discovered does not damage the texture or grain of the leather.

In mid-August the young hunters are eager to set off inland on foot with their families. Here they hunt the

---

*This fish derives its popular name from the Gaelic *ceara*, meaning "red."

small bands of caribou that graze the southern slopes of the higher ground. In the hills the animals have found relief from the biting flies that have driven them from the sheltered valleys of the fawning grounds. At this time caribou skins are most suitable for clothing, so they are carefully dried and carried out in rolls. Pack-dogs often accompany the hunters, and under the unaccustomed loads they develop a peculiar walking gait.

The cool fall days bring a return to coast life and seal hunting is soon in full swing again. The Eskimo's hunting year has completed the full circle.

But though the Eskimo is primarily a lone hunter, he also shows great adaptability for community life. In the simplest meaning of the word he is a communist, who is willing to share everything with his neighbours. No one need go hungry while there is any food in an Eskimo village. Even children are shared in a sense, and child adoption is frequently practised for no other apparent reason than that the children are being shared with others. Though each camp usually has an acknowledged leader, the Eskimos' simple social system does not call for tribal chiefs. No one is obliged to follow the camp leader if he does not want to.

The success of the Eskimo way of life depends on the preservation of the individual family unit. The children respond naturally to the guidance of their parents, but they are given every opportunity to develop and fit themselves for life. Childhood is an early phase of their training where the problems and incidents of life are presented in miniature. Isolation from others of the tribe inflicts no hardship on the mind of this primitive people. In this state they are more provident, since the whole family devotes much time to fishing, hunting and trapping.

Any opportunity to participate in community life is welcomed by the Eskimo. They delight in these in-

frequent gatherings—usually between seasons—and enjoy
all the pleasures of meeting friends and exchanging gossip.
These meetings usually mean endless rounds of visiting.
There is also an emotional experience during the wildly
picturesque drum dancing, during which the singer relates
his experience in song, accompanied by a chanting chorus of
women. Swaying easily to the rhythmic music of the
singers surrounding him, the drummer beats the time on the
hoop of the one-sided drum and often captivates his audience
with cleverly improvised footwork and strikingly realistic
sound effects.

These communal gatherings generally take place in the
spring. Gradually the ice-edge moves into the bays and
inlets as the brisk winds and motion of the waters carry the
rotting ice far out to sea. Sleds laden with seals daily
arrive at the villages and there is a happy mingling of
relatives and friends.

Cooking is now done outdoors in primitive fashion with
moss, willows or driftwood for fuel. Over the sizzling fires
are hung oblong tin kettles which I have never seen anywhere else. It might well be that they have been copied
from an older form of stone cooking pot.

These communal get-togethers sometimes end with an
ooyook or feast of boiled meat, pieces of which are circulated
with the fingers from the common pot. Several pieces are
on the move at one time. Each visitor takes the meat
offered, fills the mouth and cuts enough off with an upward
stroke of the knife. All are vocal in praise of the host, and
it is quite in good taste to belch loudly in appreciation.

Frequently the social customs of the Eskimo were influenced by the *angnacook* or medicine man, or by the "Old
Woman" who laid down certain rules of conduct for the
younger women. The influence of these tribal soothsayers
has greatly declined, but the wearing of amulets or specially

Rugged and dramatic scenery marks the face of the land between the Mackenzie Valley and the Yukon boundary. Here the Pulpit Rock on the South Nahanni River faces a sheer wall thousands of feet high.   R. M. Patterson

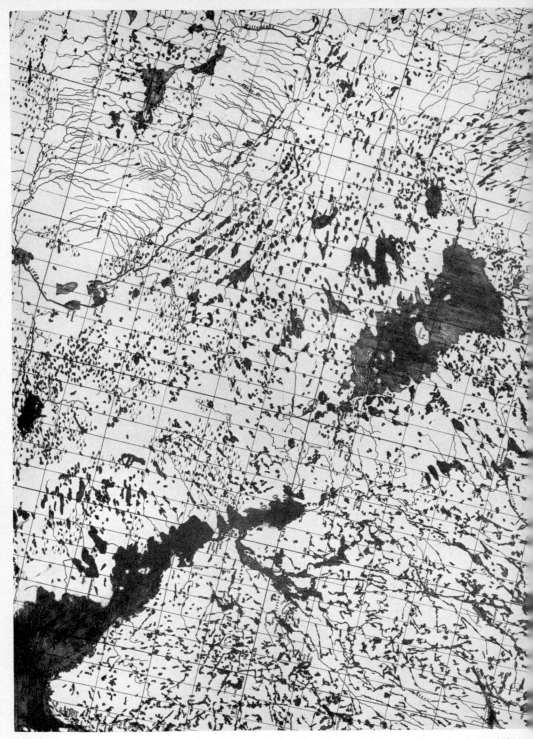

Map II. A section of the Northwest Territories between Great Slave Lake (lower left) and Great Bear Lake (upper right) which clearly shows the different characteristics of the

Precambrian Shield lakeland and the Interior Lowlands. In the latter, glaciation has not disturbed the drainage pattern like it has in the former.

Defence Research Board

H.M.S. "Alert" caught in the ice of Robeson Channel between Greenland and Ellesmere Island, in August 1876. She had spent the previous winter in Lat. 82° 30'—
... ... by the Canadian Government for service in the Arctic.

Geo. White

Richard Harrington.

An Eskimo drives his dog team in the "fan hitch" used in the Eastern Arctic.

A kyak race in Hudson Strait.   H. Bassett

Eskimo hunter with a frozen seal.   R. Harrington

Indian family in northern Manitoba.   Harrington for HBC

Chipewyan children.   Harrington for HBC

Drying meat, northern British Columbia.   Harrington for HBC

Scraping a moose hide.   Ralph Cash

decorated garments, which could be explained away as a fashion cult, might be a wistful regard for the old ways.

Much has been written about the types of winter dwelling used by the Eskimo which gives a false impression that the igloo is now obsolete. It is true that certain groups of Eskimo, particularly those living in the Mackenzie Delta and Ungava Bay, have discarded the snowhouse. For the majority of the Canadian Eskimo, however, it is home for five or possibly six months of each year. Thus they retain the skill and proficiency which makes it possible to carve a home from any suitable snowdrift.

The degree of comfort present in an igloo depends on the clothing worn and the method of heating the structure. At all times during winter and under most conditions the loose-fitting, well ventilated skin garments will give maximum protection. People living near the coast use the shallow semi-circular soapstone lamp for heating, using pounded seal-fat for fuel which feeds a moss wick placed along the straight edge. This form of heating delivers an even temperature throughout the dome-like structure. Ventilation is through the open, floor-level door and out through a small hole in the roof, which is always off centre and usually over the lamp.

There are several unpleasant things about the snowhouse, especially that of the coast-dwellers. The glistening white walls of a newly built igloo soon glaze over. Unless additional ventilation is provided—the lack of which is usually indicated by poorly burning lamps—there is an unpleasant dripping from the thawing walls. The acrid odour of rancid oil which is always present from the burning lamp, and the appearance of the raw meat piled on the floor, are things that remain as lasting impressions.

The Eskimo who live inland stay close to one of the great lakes which lie in the path of the migrating caribou herds.

Since caribou skins are usually plentiful, they are more warmly clad than the people of the coast. A single flame from a deer fat "dip" is therefore enough to give light in the igloo, and cooking is done in a snow annex with willow brush or moss for fuel. An inland igloo usually smells of deerskin clad humans and the peculiar odour of frozen fish, which are generally stacked in one part of the snowhouse.

In the spring the long grip of winter is quickly broken. Heavy snowfall followed by periods of strong sunshine plays havoc with the snowhouses, regardless of the loose snow shovelled over them for insulation. Trapping is now over, and the families move to the traditional spring hunting grounds. Tents are recovered from under the melting snows and soon groups of tents appear on the long points and sandspits that command a wide view of the sea ice where seals now bask in the warm sunshine. Drying racks are erected in readiness for skins and meat and soon the spring hunt is in progress.

Canvas tents are now popular, but occasionally there may be seen the old bell-shaped skin tent or *tupik* which for centuries has served the Eskimo well. Throughout the great islands of the Arctic and along the coast can still be found the moss-grown tent rings of stone, which served to hold down the sides of the tents inhabited by the Eskimos of long ago. These odd looking tents have many advantages over the modern canvas tents; they will withstand terrific wind pressure without sagging, they give excellent protection from rain or driving snow and winter's cold, and in summer their cool, dark interiors are avoided by biting flies and similar winged pests.

Every race, no matter how primitive, has its poets and its artists. In the case of the Eskimos their cultural life has been more devoted to improving their lot than to the pursuit of the more familiar forms of the arts. With the possession of finer tools and some encouragement from out-side sources, some striking examples of creative art have been produced and have been acclaimed by collectors as excellent pieces of sculpture in a pure, untutored form. Although the Eskimo race has not yet brought forth any versatile artist, there are in existence collections of stories and songs that reveal the poetic nature of the people.

Yet their folklore reveals nothing of their history or racial accomplishments, and we can only conclude that some great influence of the past has given them that strength of character and tenacity of purpose which is almost un-equalled. Their traditional way of life remains unchanged. The majority of the Canadian Eskimo prefer to live as their forefathers did. Strange as they may appear in our eyes, these rugged, skin-clad people form a nation that has pre-served all that is good from the past. They have admired but never marvelled at the white man's genius, and have adopted only certain equipment that his more inventive mind has devised.

The virtue of patience and the skill of the hands that have for centuries carved ivory, bone and flotsam into mar-vellous hunting weapons, has made possible such mechanical arts as the reproduction of engine parts when otherwise it would have been impossible to get them. I have seen piston rings made and fitted and threads cut with a file that would be acknowledged as excellent workmanship by any standard.

For centuries the Eskimo have allowed white men to penetrate their country and have steadfastly maintained the right to speak their own language, although they have accepted the white man's laws and his religion. Since contacts with civilization have now become more frequent they have also suffered much from the diseases of the white race. Yet they willingly assist medical research teams in studies that will possibly bring more benefit to the white race than to their own. It is natural to ask—could some of this have been avoided? Is it necessary to do these things that might possibly change their lives?

And what will become of this splendid people? The modern trend is towards education and assimilation with other Canadian peoples. It is too soon to predict the out' come, but it is certain that this alone will not ensure their survival, while it may rob them of that perfect understand' ing of their way of life. There is need for a complete understanding of the arctic economy while the mistakes and lessons of the past are still clear. The Canadian Eski' mo is not, to use a modern expression, under'privileged. A rich, satisfying life is there for them if we can intelligently interpret their needs and use all available means to stabilize the arctic economy by ensuring fair and just prices for the by'products of their hunting, or by some practical scheme of assistance when their living standards are endangered through no fault of their own.

The Eskimos are a proud race who call themselves *Innuit* —"The People." Elsewhere this has been translated as "men pre'eminently," signifying a belief in their ability to meet and overcome the storms and stresses of their daily existence, which requires the qualities of a Man in every sense of the word.

Leonard Butler, M.Sc., Ph.D., is professor of zoology at the University of Toronto. For seven years he was fur trade biologist with the Hudson's Bay Company in Winnipeg, studying the diseases and forecasting the cycles of fur bearing animals throughout the North.

Mammals of Land and Sea

by LEONARD BUTLER

I--Four Feet

SEVERAL years ago, travellers on the "Muskeg Special" which runs from The Pas to Churchill, were suddenly jolted from their seats as the train came to an unexpected stop. When they were able to pick themselves up from the floor, or from the corners into which they had been thrown, they were rewarded with a spectacle which made up for any discomfort they had suffered. The annual migration of caribou was crossing the tracks and surging around the train. It took almost an hour for the herd to pass, and the trampled ground along the right-of-way indicated it was almost half a mile wide at this point.

It was migrations of this sort which made travellers think that there were millions of caribou wandering around the arctic wastes, and until recently people were reluctant to admit that the herds have been so decimated that concern must be expressed for their survival. The reason for this decrease has been variously attributed to overhunting, the introduction of the high powered rifle, careless slaughter for tongues, the impinging of civilization on their migration routes, increased predation by wolves, and inclement weather. One year the Quebec herd was reduced greatly by a February thaw, followed by a freeze which left the ground covered with glare ice. The caribou could not paw through this to get at their food of lichens and moss, so they starved to death. Whatever the reasons may have been for their decrease in numbers, a concerted effort is now being made to find out more about the animal so that the herds may be restored to something like their original numbers.

Caribou are very similar to reindeer and were often called reindeer or deer by the English speaking settlers, but gradually the term reindeer has been replaced by the word "caribou" of Algonkian origin, used by the French and half-breed population. There are two main types of caribou—the barren-ground and the woodland. The barren-ground type is a medium-sized (350-400 pounds) rather stocky animal with a thick neck. Antlers are borne by both sexes, those of the male being much larger, palmate at the tips and having a brow tine which extends over the face. The colour varies with season and species. In general the male in autumn is dark brown with white neck and chest and a white rump patch and tail. The colour fades greatly and by the next summer it may be tan or nearly whitish. The males drop their antlers in November and December, while the females drop theirs later, sometimes keeping them until May or June at about the time that the single young is born. This animal is extremely important in the economy of the Eskimo; its flesh is used for food, its skin for clothing, bedding, tents, lashings, harpoon lines, etc., its sinews and bones for sewing, and its fat for heat and light.

Migrations have always been the subject of a great deal of speculation. The Indians thought that the southern migration to the woods was made up entirely of males who had lost their antlers and were seeking shelter until their new ones grew. The females were thought to stay as separate herds in the barren lands. Most white naturalists thought the herds were made up of both sexes, and some even went so far as to say that each herd was led by a large female. It is now known that there are several separate herds of caribou and that each have their own migration route. In general these routes are southward in October and November into the bush country and northward in March and April to the arctic tundra. There are still many unknowns concerning the size of the various herds and their migration routes but it is hoped that aerial reconnaissance and photography will clear up some of these mysteries.

The Woodland caribou is slightly larger than its Barrenland cousin, and spends all its life in the bush country to the south of the tundra. It also feeds on moss and lichens but is less gregarious than the Barrenland type. Woodland caribou are not as wary of hunters and predators as are the deer and moose, and therefore have been reduced almost to extinction over much of their former range.

Roaming the valley and plains of the Thelon River one finds small herds of *Musk Ox*. This animal looks like a cross between a cow and a ram. It has a stocky body which is covered with very long hair that forms a fringe below its belly. The most conspicuous feature of the musk ox is its horns; these occur in both sexes and are extremely broad at the base so that most of the forehead is covered with them. This animal is well adapted to its mode of life and capable of making its living on a comparatively small area of the barrens. It does not migrate but gets its food in winter by clearing away the snow with its nose and hoofs and feeding on the underlying grass and moss. The animals move about their range in small herds, and when attacked and brought to bay, they gather in a close group with heads out to ward off the enemy.   This habit has been their undoing in contact with man, and they are now fully protected to prevent extinction.   It is a slow-breeding animal with palatable flesh, a hide which makes a warm robe, and horns which make useful weapons and utensils.

To endure the long cold winters of this northern country its animals are often provided with thick fur coats; therefore it is not surprising to find that many of the furs in milady's wardrobe come from this area.   One furbearer of great economic importance to the Eskimo is the white or *Arctic Fox* which, because of the cyclic nature of its populations, intermittently subjects the Eskimo to prosperity in peak years and poverty every fourth year when the cycle is at its low.   This cycle in abundance is so spectacular that a visitor to the Arctic in a peak year sees foxes close to, or even in the settlements, whereas in a year of population scarcity no fox will be seen in many days of travel.

An arctic fox is about two thirds the size of the common red fox which it resembles, but differs from in the following points.   Its snout is broader and shorter, its legs are shorter and its feet are covered with hair.   Also the ears are smaller, rounded and covered with hair making them hardly noticeable in the long winter coat.   This animal exists in two colour phases, white and blue.   The white phase has a pelt of long snow-white hairs with short, dense smoky-grey underfur, and against this background the dark eyes and black nose stand out clearly.   The "blue" phase, which is greyish-brown with white hairs scattered over the body, closely resembles the summer coat for both phases —a smoky-brown colour with no long hair.

The arctic fox makes its burrows in the sandy or peaty soils of the tundra or in crevices in the rock generally not far from the coast. In these burrows in April and May the 3 to 15 young are born. Both parents assist in rearing the young, and in catching lemming which is their main food. In summer they usually live well on the eggs and young of duck, geese, gulls, and other water birds, along with fish and white whales thrown up by the sea. Old foxes often follow a polar bear so they can devour the remains of its kill.

The Mackenzie River area and the Yukon provide excellent habitat for the alert and inquisitive *Marten*, one of the more valuable fur bearers. Its curiosity makes it easy to trap and has led to a ten-fold reduction in the population. Marten are very nimble-footed and are quite at home in trees where they can even catch the elusive squirrel. Their food consists chiefly of small mammals, birds and their eggs, frogs, fish, insects and berries.

Two of the marten's cousins also live in this area—the fisher and the mink. The *Fisher* does not fish, in fact it rarely goes near the water. It was given that name because of its fondness for bait made from fish. Fisher eat much the same food as the marten with the addition of porcupine, for it is one of the few animals which can take quills in its face and food without too much harm. The fisher is the largest of the weasel family, and while his size and agility make him a formidable adversary even for man, he has never become numerous because of his slow reproductive rate.

Mink, on the other hand, do become numerous especially during the cyclic peaks which occur every ten years. This animal, which wears its own mink coat, is a bloodthirsty hunter that often kills for the love of killing. Mink can also be playful, and like the otter, will slide on their bellies down a mud- or snow-covered slope, then run back up again to repeat the performance. The mink coat of Fifth Avenue bears little resemblance to the raw skin, for the dressed pelt has been cut into strips about half an inch wide and then sewn together again to make the pelt longer and to accentuate the dark strip down the center of the back.

The Indian, snowshoeing along his trapline in quest of the rich furs of fisher, marten and mink, has a malicious enemy in the *Wolverine* or carcajou. This beast has a heavy-built body mounted on short strong legs and its feet are armed with sharp claws. The wolverine is credited with diabolical cunning and persistence. It has been known to follow a trapper making the rounds of his trapline, in order to spring the trap and remove the bait. Often it will pull the traps from their anchors to carry them away and hide them. When the trapper awakes in his camp he is liable to find that the wolverine has taken his axe away and hidden it, and after being harassed in this manner for some time the timid trapper sometimes abandons his trapline altogether. The wolverine covers large tracts of country in its ceaseless search for food and mischief. Because of its strength and cunning he has earned a special place for himself in Eskimo folklore. Many hunters wear belts made from the skin of the head and legs of the wolverine so that they will acquire some of the hunting prowess of this animal. The fur is coarse, dark brown with lighter coloured stripes along each side of the back, and it is mostly used for parka trimming because it does not collect and hold moisture from the breath as easily as other furs.

In the delta regions of the Mackenzie and Athabasca Rivers the *Muskrat* is a major fur bearer. This animal is three or four times as large as the house rat to which it bears a superficial resemblance. Its hind feet are partly webbed to aid in swimming, and its hairless, scaly tail, flattened vertically makes a good rudder. In marshes the muskrats build roughly conical houses of roots and stems of plants with a mixture of mud. One or more oval chambers are chewed out of the interior above the water level, and entrance to these chambers is gained by passageways with openings under water. In winter the muskrat does not normally come out into the open air above the ice, but spends the five months confined to its house and the water below the ice. During this time he is forced to breathe either the stale air of his house or the air contained in bubbles under the ice. In breathing the latter, the muskrat swims up to the bubble, breathes out, and then fills his lungs. The remaining air he leaves in the bubble to pick up oxygen from the water so that it will be ready for his next trip in the vicinity. The muskrat, unlike his close relative the beaver, which also occurs in this region, does not cut down trees or build dams and canals. He lives on the roots of aquatic plants and seeks out marshes where the natural water levels are suitable. Muskrats are prolific breeders; they have two or three litters a year with five to ten young in each litter. Like many other animals, when a litter is due they drive out the older litter to fend for themselves. The mother muskrat is not as subtle as the mother bear in Disney's *Bear Country*, and the sixweekold young may be badly bitten before they realize they are no longer wanted. These displaced youngsters often take up lodgings with an old male who may share his shelter with several halfgrown litters.

The cat family is represented north of 55° by the *Canada Lynx* which is about five times as large as a domestic cat, has a large head, a small stump of a tail, long hind legs and enormous feet which permit the lynx to glide over the deep snow. If scared, the lynx runs away with great leaps which have the adverse effect of causing it to sink into the snow. When forced to, it will take to water and swim a

straight course towards its destination regardless of what is
in the way or of what awaits it at the other end.   It shows
the same one-track mind in its choice of food, feeding almost
exclusively on the snowshoe rabbit, and starving when this
animal disappears.

The *Snowshoe Rabbit* or Varying Hare is the common
rabbit of this region.   It is brownish-grey in summer and
white in winter.   After the fall molt the hind feet are
covered with a heavy growth of hair which forms a broad
snowshoe-like pad, enabling the rabbit to move freely over
the soft snow.   Populations of this animal show regular
cycles of abundance and scarcity, with a ten-year stretch
from one peak abundance to the next.   The *Arctic Hare*
which occurs farther north is about twice the size of the
snowshoe rabbit and has longer hair.

The characteristic rodent of the Arctic is the *Lemming*,
which resembles a small stout rat, with a short stumpy tail
and prominent curved teeth.   The lemming is mainly
nocturnal and lives in burrows in the tundra where it is very
active throughout the winter, making a network of feeding
tunnels along the surface of the ground under the snow.
In the nests, during the early summer, the litter of from two
to eight young is born.   There are several litters a year
so that when conditions are favourable the population can
increase with great rapidity.   Lemming feed entirely on
vegetation and show such voracity that in years when they
are abundant they may denude the ground of plant life.
There are two main types of lemming in Canada: brown and
collared.   The brown lemming has the same bright brown
coat all the year around, while the collared lemming changes
its brown summer coat to a white one in winter.

Lemming migrations are well-known in Norway where
hordes of these rodents erupt from the mountain slopes and
pour down the fiords to the sea.   When they reach the sea

they swim out until they become exhausted and drown. In Canada there are no records of migrations of this type although mass movements have been noted both in Baffin- land and in the Western Arctic. In the latter area after one of the mass movements dead lemming were picked up off the sea-ice miles from any land. While the data on migrations are meagre, the population changes are well documented. Lemming populations were at their peak over most of Arctic Canada in 1934, '37, '41, '45 and 1950, thus showing a four-year cycle from peak to peak.

The *Polar Bear* remains white all the year and is es- sentially an arctic animal. It differs from its cousin the brown bear by its longer neck and smaller head, and by the fact that the soles of its feet are covered with fur. Polar bear live permanently on the ice and snow of the arctic regions, coming south with the winter extension of the ice and retreating north with the summer thaw. Some- times the odd bear is left stranded in southern waters and provides an unusual sight on either the Atlantic or Pacific coast. In winter the bears may come on land to a limited extent and may den up for awhile in crevices between rocks or pack ice, but they do not hibernate. While in this den the female gives birth to one or two small naked cubs. They stay in the den until they are old enough to travel with their mother who nurses them for eighteen months, hunts for them, and protects them until they are fully grown. Except in the case of the mother and cubs the polar bear is a solitary animal which ranges far and wide over the ice pack in search of food. This hunting is done mostly by scent rather than by sight and hearing which are somewhat dull. Its food consists chiefly of seals and young walrus which it catches on the ice, for although the bear is a good swimmer it is not fast enough to catch its prey in the water.   When it makes a kill, the bear gorges itself on the carcass and may eat as much as one hundred and fifty pounds of meat in one feed.

II—*Flippers*

In Canadian waters there are several species of *Hair Seal*, so called to distinguish them from the fur seal which is found only in the North Pacific and the islands of the Bering Sea.   The hind limbs of seal are useless for walking so they spend most of their time swimming in water or resting on ice floes.   When there is no open water in the vicinity, the seals keep breathing holes open in the ice. After swimming under the ice in search of their food, which consists of fish, crayfish and squids, they come up through these holes for air.   Hair seals usually gather into small herds at the breeding season but they do not form harems as the fur seal does.   The young, which are born in the spring, have a woolly white coat and stay uncovered on the ice for some time after their birth.   The female has a single pup each year.

The *Harbour Seal* is found in several northern lakes as well as in coastal waters.   The hair of this seal has a fur-like quality and is used for fancy work and trimming.   The *Ringed* or *Jar Seal* is found along the coasts of both the Eastern and Western Arctic and is the chief article of food for some Eskimo groups.   The dehaired skin is used for waterproof boots and kayak covers, while the haired skin is used for other garments.   The *Bearded Seal* is the largest of the hair seals, some specimens weighing over 800 pounds.   Its teeth are weak and rounded so that it cannot catch fish as easily as the other seals and has to subsist largely on shellfish and crayfish.   Its skin is tougher and is cut into heavy lines for dog traces, harpoon lines, and lashings for sleds. It was also used as a cover for the large skin boat or *oomiak*.

In Canadian waters the *Walrus* occurs only as far west as Fury and Hecla Straits. It was formerly hunted ex-tensively for the ivory of its tusks, and the population has now been severely reduced. They are now protected and hunting is restricted to Eskimos who need the flesh, oil and skins. The characteristic appearance of the walrus is brought about by the strong bristles of the upper lip which produce the familiar moustache. The canine teeth of the upper jaw are greatly elongated into curved tusks which reach a length of thirty inches. These tusks are used for loosening from the ocean floor the shellfish which constitute the principal food of the walrus. To obtain them it dives to the bottom of the ocean, and standing almost on its head, it moves backwards digging a furrow with its tusks. Any shellfish that are rooted out along with the odd stone for good measure are swallowed whole. The walrus is a slow breeder having a single pup every two years. These pups nurse their mother for almost two years until their tusks are three to four inches long and big enough for them to obtain their own food.

III—Flukes

The *Narwhal* is a whale which has lost all its teeth except two on its upper jaw and these never break through the skin of the female. In the male, the left one erupts and grows into a spirally twisted horn some four to eight feet long and weighing ten to fourteen pounds. Growing to about fifteen feet in length, the narwhal has a spotted skin which becomes white in older animals. The purpose of the tusk is not known but fantastic stories have been told about it. One ingenious suggestion is that the tusk is twisted so that it can drill through the thick ice and make a breathing hole.*   Males have been observed to cross their tusks like rapiers in a fencing match so it is believed that they may be used as weapons.   The single horn was probably the origin of the fabled Unicorn—in fact early Arctic explorers often refer to them as such.   The narwhal is widely dispersed in the Arctic Ocean and like all whales it has no external ears, minute eyes, and a coat which is almost devoid of hair.

The *White Whale* or beluga occurs quite extensively in the arctic seas and in the waters of Hudson Bay.   It also ascends rivers in search of the fish on which it feeds.   The white whale has a voice and the name "Sea Canary" has been applied to it, but the name is not apt.   The adults are white, but the nursing young are black and gradually pale as they advance to maturity.   The adults reach lengths of ten to fifteen feet, and are hunted for their blubber which is rendered into oil, and for their skin and flesh.   The skin is used in civilization for making fine leather goods.   Over it is a layer of cork-like substance—*muktuk*—which the Eskimo considers a delicacy to be eaten raw or partly cooked.

The Right or *Greenland Whale* also occurs in this region but is not plentiful.   When whaling grounds in the vicinity of Spitsbergen began to show signs of depletion, the whalers moved into Davis Strait, Baffin Bay, and Hudson Bay, but they soon depleted this area and it no longer supports a whaling industry.

The mammals discussed here are not, of course, the only kind to be found north of 55°.   But they are typical of the area, and though many of them are also found south of 55°, they represent an interesting cross-section of animal life in the Arctic and Subarctic.

---

*Another is that when it spears a fish, it has only to swim rapidly forward to send the fish spinning like a propeller into its mouth!

The depletion of the populations of the walrus, whales, and caribou are of major concern in an economy which is still dependent on its natural resources, and show that here, where the chance discovery of a caribou migration, whale carcass, or other source of food, may be a matter of life or death to Eskimo bands or marooned travellers, the proper management of these animals is of prime importance.

Probably the most noteworthy feature of the mammal life of this region is the fluctuation of certain species between abundance and scarcity.

Clifford P. Wilson, the editor of this book, has edited the Beaver, *a magazine of the North, published by the Hudson's Bay Company, since 1939. He also edited* The New North in Pictures *and* Northern Exposures, *both books of* Beaver *photographs.*

Furs for the White Man

by CLIFFORD WILSON

UNDER a cold white moon the wide arctic land lies lifeless and forlorn. As far as the eye can see, nothing stirs in all that vast treeless expanse but a low black dot moving slowly far out on the frozen sea. As it approaches, it gradually resolves itself into a sled and dog team, with one man running beside it and one riding. They are travelling by night, not because they choose to, but because at this mid-winter season far north of the Arctic Circle, there is little or no day.

Approaching the land, they swing round a rocky point and come in sight of a group of buildings whose windows cast a welcoming golden light over the snow. It is the end of their long journey—the fur-traders' post where they will exchange the furs on their sled for the goods of the white man.

Then ensues a scene that has been repeated many thousands of times, in one form or another, throughout northern Canada since first the white man came to trade there. Warned by the howling of the dogs about the post, the post manager with his clerk and native men-servants come forward to greet the visitors. There is much hand-shaking—and much smiling. The travellers unharness the dogs and unpack the sled, then go to the native house where they are given the traditional "mug-up" of hot strong tea.

When they have finished, they gather up the fox-skins they have brought and are taken to see the post manager in his office at the back of the store. This is the Big Moment —the talk with the Boss. Speaking their language, the manager calls them by name, asks after their welfare and that of their families, all of whose names and ages he is familiar with. He learns all the family news—births, marriages, deaths, and if there has been any sickness since their last visit. They talk about the weather, the hunting, the dogs —anything but the reason for the two men's visit. The code must be observed. Finally the talk drifts round to the scarcity or otherwise of white foxes. With apparent reluctance the two Eskimos, who have protested up to this point that their catch has been a poor one, place some of their best fox skins on the table.

One by one the manager appraises them, jots down their value, and gives each customer a slip of paper to hand to the clerk who is waiting for them, clad in his outdoor clothes, in the unheated store.

Now, confronted by the breath-taking array of white men's goods neatly arranged on the long shelves, the two men remain speechless for some time. While they wonder what to ask for first, the clerk puts out small piles of metal discs on the counter in denominations of 5, 10, 25, 50 and 100, each representing so many cents. Beside these he places piles of square counters stamped with the figure 1, each representing one fox skin—one for each skin that the customer has brought in.

Before trading can begin, however, some of these tokens must be deducted. Each Eskimo, according to the im-memorial practice of the fur trade, has a certain amount of debt outstanding on the trader's books, which depends on the size of his family and his ability as a trapper. That is to say, he has previously bought some goods on credit, and now that he has some skins to trade, he pays his debt before buying anything else. Tokens representing the amount of the debt are therefore removed from the piles on the counter, so that each Eskimo can see exactly what he has to spend.

Presently one of them remembers that he has brought with him a list that his wife, back in the home igloo, has made up for him. From the recesses of his caribou-skin *artiggi* he produces a grimy bit of paper with some characters pencilled on it in syllabic writing. And he begins to place his order.

First and foremost he buys some tobacco. As each item is taken off the shelves and placed on the counter, the clerk makes change from the tokens. If the current value of a fox skin is ten dollars, and the first item the Eskimo chooses is worth four, the clerk takes away one of the square counters and substitutes six 100's. Then if the next item purchased is worth $2.75, the clerk takes away three 100's and substitutes one 25. This process is repeated until the native's order is filled. If he has any tokens left, the amount is credited to his account. But usually he over-shoots the mark and all the discs have disappeared before he has bought all he wants to.

As the Eskimo sees the counters diminishing he becomes more choosy, and takes longer and longer to make up his mind. The patient clerk tries to help him, advising against the buying of things that will please him for only a short time and be of little use in the long run, and suggesting instead the purchase of really practical goods. Finally,

after much indecision and discussion, the last metal token
goes back into the drawer.

When the native finds he has come to the end of his
tether he may decide that something he bought near the
beginning of the trade is not very desirable after all.   He
hands it back and asks for something else that he considers
more necessary.   Finally, when he can think of no more to
ask for, he goes off and sits down while the tokens are
produced again from the drawer and the other man starts to
go through *his* list.

That, in brief, is how fur trading is usually conducted in
the eastern Canadian Arctic by the traditional barter
system.   It is a slow, unhurried process, for the Eskimo
has all the time in the world.   But in most parts of the
north this system has been abandoned in favour of cash
transactions.   The numbered discs of the eastern Arctic
are designed to teach the Eskimo how to count so that
eventually cash will supplant tokens in that area also.   In
the western Arctic, where the natives have more frequent
contact with the Outside, this change has already taken
place.

Throughout the North, in fact, the fur trade is rapidly
becoming modernized, and with the passing of the old ways,
much of the "romance" has departed also.   Many of the
old-timers regret this, and complain—as old-timers do
everywhere, and probably have done since the first stirrings
of civilization—that things aren't what they used to be.

Not more than five years ago, for instance, a Scot who
had spent a generation trading in the Arctic left that lonely
land because he said the adventure had gone out of it. Time
was when he had travelled hundreds of miles by dog-team,
and slept every night of his winter journeys in snowhouses,
just in the ordinary course of business, visiting the Eskimo
camps to make and renew friendships, buy up the furs they

had collected, give advice on community problems, and minister to the sick.

A skilful sailor, he had navigated small schooners through uncharted waters far along the Arctic coast; and on one occasion he had been shipwrecked in an autumn gale with a team of dogs on board, kept himself alive by eating seagulls and some of the dogs, and when the sea froze hard enough, setting out for the nearest trading post with what remained of the dogs and a small sled he had built out of the boat wreckage.

That couldn't happen today. In a matter of a few days a search plane would locate him, pick him up, and whisk him back to the post—all with the proper amount of news-paper publicity. For today the Arctic is overrun with communications. It is no longer a land where a hardy Scot can live for a year or more without seeing another white man; where he is on his own until the next annual ship comes in, completely out of touch with his boss, and where he can feel like the monarch of all he surveys.

Today he can no longer adventure forth on long trips to the native camps, or go hunting for seal or walrus. He has to stay at the post to maintain his regular radio "skeds" and keep in daily touch with the Outside. His trading store, once a somewhat nondescript shack where systematic arrangement was not particularly noticeable, is now a spick-and-span, white clapboarded building with scarlet roof, designed by some city architect, where goods are displayed according to plan, and which looks for all the world like an up-to-date general store.

To be sure, some picturesque characters are still to be found in that store—the Eskimos who bring in the frozen fox skins from their primitive camps. But they are soon gone, back to the snowhouse or the summer tent, far away along the barren shore where the fur trader is now almost a stranger.

So the Scotsman of many adventures came south. For you're no longer a real fur trader up there today, as he said—just an Arctic storekeeper.

And that, perhaps, is a sign of the times. For in these days of social security, when comfort is considered an end in itself, adventure doesn't appeal to the young men like it did a generation or two ago. To keep them happy in the far north, they have to be supplied with many of the luxuries they have become accustomed to—with a radio, a few shelves of books, a varied stock of food, comfortable furniture, and framed pictures.

The isolation which the resourceful old-timer found so satisfying is now to be shunned in favour of as much contact with the Outside as possible—a craving which can be the more easily gratified through the medium of the ubiquitous radio. The female element is partly responsible for this modernization—or softening up, as some regard it. A generation ago, not many far northern post managers were married. Today, most of them are. Of the modern far north it may be truly said, "Women are here to stay." Perhaps then, there is still romance in the fur trade, but of a different sort.

On the business, rather than the social, side, the modern-ization of the fur trade may be summed up in the one word "merchandising." In the old days, when there was no white trade to speak of, the fur trader left merchandising to the buyers in the cities who provided him with trade goods —though he did not always approve of what they bought him to trade. He concentrated on the furs themselves. But today it is not enough to know a good skin when you see one. You must also know your merchandise and its selling points. This isn't so necessary in the remoter posts,

where your clientele is mostly made up of Indians and
Eskimos.   There the problem is not to persuade the customer to buy, but to discourage him from buying what he
doesn't need.   It is in the more civilized posts, where the
white trade is a factor to be reckoned with, that one encounters sales resistance.

Because the fur trade deals in two forms of buying and
selling instead of one, it is different from most businesses.
In most forms of trade, the trader buys at wholesale for
money and sells at retail for money, and that completes the
transaction.   But in the fur trade he buys goods at wholesale and sells them at retail, either for furs or for cash with
which he buys furs.   And having bought the furs at retail,
he must turn around and sell them to a dealer in raw furs at
wholesale.   He therefore has two chances of making a
profit—or a loss.

Besides these chances, the fur trader must be willing to
take plenty of other risks, especially in the more northern
latitudes.   In the main the risks he runs are dependent on
the feminine whims of two well known flighty characters
often referred to as Mother Nature and Dame Fashion.
The latter lays down the law—with the illogicality that
might be expected from one of her sex—as to the prices that
will eventually be paid for raw furs in the city.   The
former governs the supply, which is equally unpredictable.

A fur trader in the Arctic, for instance, being informed
that prices for white fox in the markets of the world are
reasonably high, and knowing that foxes that winter are
plentiful, buys up all he can lay his hands on at good prices.
Next summer the supply ship calls with the following
season's supply of trade goods and takes out the furs.   In
the meantime, however, those who decree what will be
worn this year in the world of fashion have decided—for
some totally unaccountable reason—that white fox will not

be. And when the previous winter's catch reaches the city's auctions, the arctic fox market has slumped. Thus the trader, who has gone to great expense shipping in trade goods and bringing out the furs, takes a heavy loss.

On the other hand, both Fashion and Nature may favour him. He may buy his foxes when the market price is low, and sell them when it is high. In other years, Nature may be against him and Fashion for him, or vice versa.

There are also considerable risks to be taken in the matter of transportation—the life line of the fur trade. One of the chief characteristics of the trade is that the raw material is to be found a long way from where the finished product is sold, so that a great deal depends on shipping the raw furs from the wilderness where they are caught to the cities where they are auctioned. By the same token, trade goods manufactured in the cities must be shipped a long way to the wilderness posts where they are sold to the trappers. As much of the transportation of furs and goods must be across almost uninhabited areas of the North, the danger of loss or delay is considerably greater than it is by regular routes within the confines of civilization. Canoes and dog teams may have given way to motor vessels and airplanes, and the "moccasin telegraph" to two-way radio; but no matter how the methods of communication have been modernized, the relentless forces of Nature have always to be reckoned with. A plane may not be able to land because the ice on the lakes is too strong for floats and too weak for skis. A ship may be held up by ice, or may even be lost with her cargo of goods and furs by striking an uncharted rock. When the famous *Nascopie* was sunk in this way in 1947 with the year's supply of trade goods and provisions for most of the Eastern Arctic posts, it meant that another year's supply had to be hastily bought up and another vessel chartered to take them north.   The lost furs could not of course be replaced.

But the trader is not the only one to take great risks in this business of fur buying and selling.   The trapper* also must reckon with the uncertainties of wilderness life and travel, and with the whims of Fashion; and it must be even more bewildering to the native than it is to the white man when the price of fur suddenly and unaccountably drops.

North of 55° the trappers are mostly natives—Indians, Eskimos and half-breeds.   In the Northwest Territories the only white men who are allowed to trap are those who have held licences continually since 1939—for the fur trade is still the main source of livelihood for natives north of 60°.

Each trapper has his own trapline, often with small cabins built at intervals along it so that he can spend the nights in warmth and comfort.   In place of log cabins, Indians sometimes use tents, which they leave standing each a day's journey from the last.   The white trapper, who believes in being prepared, will often go round the trapline before the season starts in November, making sure that each of his cabins is well stocked with firewood and with grub that will keep, and that the fire is laid in his stove for anyone to use who is in need of it.   But the Indian, being naturally improvident, will not cut his firewood until he has to, and takes just enough food for the trip.

The male trapper—and the distinction is necessary because there are a number of experienced women trappers in the North—leaves his family at the base camp while he goes his rounds.   He may go alone, but more often he travels with one or more friends.   He walks on snowshoes, and he may either drag his own toboggan or use a team of dogs.   Some Indians of today even use planes to get to and from their trapping grounds, but that is an expensive luxury they can seldom indulge in.

---

*Here it might be well to mention the difference between a trapper and a trader.   One constantly sees references in the Press to "Hudson's Bay Company fur trappers."   But there is no such thing.   The trapper is the man who traps the animals and sells their pelts to the trader—Hudson's Bay or otherwise.   He doesn't work for the fur trading company any more than the city shopper works for the store where he shops.

The trapper's fare is simple—mostly dry meat, beans, bannock, lard and tea. For his dogs he will usually bring dried fish, or maybe oatmeal. He may take along as few as ten or as many as 200 traps of various sizes, and set them along a route that may vary from twenty to three hundred miles in length. For beaver and otter he sets traps under the ice, for mink on the bank of a lake or stream, for marten and fisher in a little "cubby" of evergreen branches in the forest. Foxes may be trapped at the base of a tree, or snared in a runway like rabbits and lynxes.

The Eskimo, whose catch is generally limited to Arctic fox, places his trap on the top of a hummock as he has noted that foxes will always walk over a mound rather than around it. Such a spot will also be free from snowdrifts which would bury a trap. All traps, of course, have to be hidden. The barrenland trapper covers his with either a very thin pan of hard snow or with moss—and he doesn't spend much time disguising his own presence there since the Arctic fox is by no means as crafty as his larger woodland cousin. The woods trapper, however, has to hide all traces of man smell, which is not easy. All sorts of bait are used, but smell is the dominating quality.

Having placed his traps, the trapper makes the round of his trapline several days later, removes the frozen animals he has caught, thaws them out, skins them, and back home gives them to his wife to stretch. There are two methods of skin stretching—open and cased. The beaver skin for instance is stretched open, which means that it is cut down the middle and taken off the carcass like an unbuttoned coat. Muskrats, foxes, mink, and similar pelts are cased—that is, the skin is pulled inside out starting at the tail and over the head, much as a man pulls off a sweater. The open skin is stretched on a hoop, the cased pelt on a thin board or frame pointed at one end.

Time was, not so long ago, when the native trapper left the trading post with his outfit of goods in the fall, and did not return till the spring.   He lived partly off the land and did not feel the need of getting back to the comparative civilization of the post until he was good and ready.   But now the Indians and Eskimos, like the rest of us, are less self-sufficient than they used to be, and they will come into the post bringing what furs they have collected about once a month, to get new supplies or join in the festivities at Christmas, New Year's and Easter.   It is the white trapper, strangely enough, who stays out in the bush for months at a time—probably because, being more provident, he doesn't live from hand to mouth, and so doesn't have to collect his Family Allowance from the Federal Government, or stock up as often as the native does.

However, there is much more than supplies for the native to get at the trading post.   In the remoter posts especially, the modern fur trader has a great deal to offer his customers besides what is seen on the shelves of his store.   The actual business of fur trading may be his chief occupation, but native welfare is one of his chief responsibilities.   Government services are being extended every year in the North, but there are still many posts where government officials do not live, and where the fur trader has to substitute for them.   Thus he is required to distribute the government's Family Allowances—in cash or in kind—and keep the vital statistics of the families who trade at his post. In matters of health he must often administer medicines and first aid, and sometimes amputate frozen fingers and toes, suture deep wounds, assist at childbirth, and even deal with the first stages of epidemics.   In this work of mercy he now has the valuable help of government doctors, who diagnose the cases as best they can and advise the trader what to do—all by radio from hundreds of miles away.

Actually, except for the medical advice, there is nothing new in this amateur doctoring. Fur traders have been doing it for years—in fact for centuries. Living far from any sources of medical care other than what is in their own hands, they have accepted such responsibilities as part and parcel of the business of fur trading among primitive peoples. And your modern trader well knows, as his bearded predecessors did before him, that taking a genuine and active interest in his customers' welfare will keep them coming back year after year, generation after generation. So besides coming to him when they are sick, the natives have the habit of asking his aid and advice in all sorts of matters, from tribal affairs to the care of firearms, from walrus hunts to family quarrels.

In the regular course of business today's trader has several other responsibilities and duties. He must know how to grade and pack and ship the furs he collects; to care for the post's machinery and equipment such as electric light plants, boats and schooners; to operate his two-way radio; to train new members of the staff; to look after the garden; and to take the greatest precautions—especially in the winter—against fire which might wipe out his stocks of furs and merchandise and his home in the wilderness.

In short, despite the tremendous increase during the past few years in the speed and efficiency of communications, and in the numbers of other white men in the North, fur trading at the remoter posts still requires the old qualities of initiative and leadership that have always been necessary in men who live far from the resources of civilization.

Lorne Manchester, assistant director of the information and educational services of the Department of Fisheries in Ottawa, joined that department in 1948, and has travelled from coast to coast studying fishing operations at first hand. He is the author of Harvest of the Waters *and* Science in Fisheries.

Fish and Fishing

by LORNE MANCHESTER

WATER is a dominating feature of Canada's northern landscape. The Yukon and Northwest Territories contain two of the earth's largest lakes and two mighty rivers, besides literally thousands of lesser virgin waters. The northern regions of the Prairie Provinces are drained by a sprawling network of lakes and rivers, some of which have not yet been explored. And bounding the entire area on three sides, with the exception of the western border of the Yukon, is the sea. The Arctic coast line alone extends roughly 10,000 miles from the Bering Sea to Hudson Strait, constituting more than half Canada's total marine frontier.

Although the mere presence of water doesn't always guarantee fish, we know that many of these northland lakes and rivers teem with great quantities of various species, some of unusual size. A few of them, like the inconnu or "conny," the Arctic grayling or "bluefish" and the Arctic char have not been found anywhere else in Canada. Others like the whitefish, the trouts, the salmon, the pike and the pickerel are familiar to most Canadians. But whether familiar or not, all these northern varieties have a special attraction. The sport fish have gained fame among the angling fraternity for their fighting characteristics, their size and their proneness to bite at almost any lure. The food fish have achieved similar recognition from the commercial operators for their cornucopia-like abundance and their table qualities. It might even be said that Canada's northland is the last stronghold of the freshwater fishes which at one time swarmed unmolested in the lakes and rivers of the now-civilized areas of Canada. This stronghold is steadily being invaded as the line of civilization pushes northward.

In the past decade a remarkable development of the north's fishery resources has taken place. The business of exporting fish is now well established in the northern areas of the three Prairie Provinces and at Great Slave Lake in the Northwest Territories. Tourist facilities have been extended to meet the demands of the increasing numbers of Canadian and United States sportsmen seeking new angling thrills in these regions each year.

Although the value of a nation's natural resource is usually considered in terms of production figures or dollars and cents, it would be misleading to look at the northern fisheries from this point of view. While the North's commercial production of freshwater fish might be worth roughly $5 million or more a year, this does not account for the significance of the resource as a food for the local populations or as a tourist attraction. The scattered communities of Indians, Eskimos and white residents north of 55° have long depended on fish for food both for themselves and their sled dogs—their chief means of transportation in the winter. While this may not be as true now as it was a few years ago in the more settled areas in the Prairie Provinces, and along the air routes to Yellowknife, Whitehorse and Dawson, it still applies in the arctic and sub-arctic regions.

More than a century ago Sir John Richardson, famous English naturalist who accompanied Franklin on his first and second expeditions into northern Canada, was amazed at the quantities of whitefish consumed by the Indians. "Several Indian hordes subsist mainly on it," he said, and "it forms the principal food at many of the fur posts for eight or nine months of the year." The nine Athapascan Indian tribes which roamed "Rupert's Land" less than two centuries ago depended mainly on fish for food. Although their descendants now have a taste for flour, bacon, beans and other "luxuries," fish is still a vital need.

Along the arctic coast, beyond the timber line, the Eskimos eat huge amounts of fish themselves and give large quantities to their dogs. The fish they get are arctic char, herring, whitefish and inconnu. The inconnu incidentally might be called a king-sized member of the whitefish family and has been found only in the Northwest and Yukon Territories. History has it that it was named by Alexander Mackenzie's intrepid French voyageurs who had never seen any fish like it before and called it the "unknown" fish. The Eskimos eat most of their fish raw and frozen. They call it *quawk* and like it slightly "high." This custom of eating raw fish gives them a supply of vitamins which they would not otherwise get in their diet.

Not a great deal is known about the fisheries resources along the arctic coast and around the islands of the District of Franklin. The Fisheries Research Board of Canada is attempting to remedy this and has a specially-constructed research boat called the *Calanus* which has been making regular trips to Eastern Arctic waters each summer since 1949. These studies are now being extended to Hudson Bay and the Beaufort Sea in the Western Arctic. Back in the thirties a fisheries expedition explored the waters of Hudson Bay and reported that there did not seem to be

BARREN GROUND CARIBOU

MUSKRAT

drawings by Clarence Tillenius

ARCTIC FOXES

MUSK OX

FISHER

MARTEN

LYNX

Setting a trap for marten. H. Bassett

Stretching a beaver skin. Harrington for HBC

Indian trappers welcomed by post manager.   Harrington for HBC

Trading at an Arctic post with tokens.   R. Harrington

Baling furs at a woodland post.

J. W. Anderson

A "line" post at Kitwanga, B.C.

Harrington for HBC

Sport fishing in the Yukon.   On the left is Viscount Alexander.   Viscount Alanbrooke

Unloading fish into a refrigerator truck on Great Slave Lake.   World News Services

Fish from the Mackenzie River being gutted and hung on a drying rack.
Henry Jones

Two Eskimos taking fish out of a net that has been set beneath the ice of the Coppermine River.
L. A. Learmonth

sufficient quantities of fish to support commercial operations. However the survey indicated there was enough fish to take care of the needs of the native inhabitants around its shores.

Dr. Max Dunbar, of McGill University, who has been in charge of the exploratory cruises on the *Calanus*, reported after his first voyage to Ungava Bay that both the Atlantic cod and the Greenland shark provided possibilities of exploitation by the Eskimo populations there. These Eskimos were not fish-minded like their cousins farther west. Traditionally game-hunters, they were suffering because of scarcity of caribou. Following Dr. Dunbar's report, the federal authorities began an experiment to educate the inhabitants to regard fish as an important source of food and to take greater advantage of the supply. An instructor-fisherman was sent to Port Burwell with fishing equipment. He spent three months showing the natives how to use it. By the end of the season's operations, they had learned to catch and preserve enough fish for their current needs.

However, the natives still prefer hunting to fishing, and they eat cod only when they can't get seal. Federal government observers who visited the area in 1953 found the natives taking advantage of the good supply of jar seals and harp seals, and not bothering to take in a winter's supply of fish despite their new knowledge of fishing technique.

The Yukon Territory, too, has its share of the better-known food and game fish. While they are important as a local food supply and as a tourist attraction, they are not significant enough to support a commercial enterprise for export purposes. The salmon runs of the Yukon River provide one of the main protein foods of white men, Indians and their dog-teams throughout the year. It is in the mighty Yukon that the indomitable king or spring salmon has achieved fame by swimming upstream 1800 miles, bucking a current all the way, to spawn in the McClintock River. This remarkable journey, which takes about twelve weeks of travel, has no known parallel among fish which come out of the sea to spawn in fresh water. The king salmon fishery is carried on below Dawson, past Moosehide and Forty-mile to the border. The Indians use gill nets set in eddies and the majority of the fish are filleted, smoked and dried for winter use. The white residents trap them with an ingenious device known as a fish-wheel, unique in Canada's commercial fisheries. It is a hollow-square raft carrying a sort of paddle wheel. Alternating with the paddles are chicken-wire scoops and as the wheel is rotated by the movement of the water each scoop dips under the surface and traps any fish swimming up against it. Something like 30,000 lbs. of fish are taken in this way every year. Both fish wheels and nets also bring in small quantities of other fish, such as the humpback or Nelson's whitefish, inconnu, and arctic grayling. Some of the salmon catch is sold fresh, and several thousand pounds are held in cold storage in Dawson City. In the southwest Yukon, according to Indian Legend, salmon used to run up the Alsek River, but some unknown obstacle now blocks their path. This river and its tributaries in the Shakwak valley contain rainbow trout, actually a landlocked steelhead, and a few land-locked sockeye salmon or *kokanee*, so that there seems to be some basis for the story.

The blockade in the Alsek seriously affects the food supply of the Indians in the southwest Yukon. However, salmon and steelhead are still able to run up the Tatsenshini tributary which enters the Alsek below the barrier and a few Indians migrate each summer to its head waters at Klukshu to catch them.

Some fishing with gill nets for domestic or commercial purposes is done in the larger Yukon lakes, and the fish taken include whitefish, lake trout and least "herring" or cisco.

The Yukon has become more accessible than ever before. Regular air services and the Alaska Highway have opened a new domain for the sports fishermen. In a setting of mountains of exceptional grandeur and beauty, in a summer climate which is genial and dry, there are many good rivers and lakes which now can be reached by the angler. Blue-fish are often so plentiful that they may be taken on a fly at the rate of thirty an hour if the waters are swift and clear and if these handsome but temperamental fighters are in the right mood. Dolly Vardens can also be caught on a fly in the eastern section and in the Tatsenshini. In the Dezadeash and Alsek there is first class rainbow trout fishing; and all the lakes contain lake trout and often large "jackfish" or pike. The number of sports fishermen visiting this northwestern tip of Canada each summer has doubled in the past four years and now exceeds 1500.

Great Bear Lake and Great Slave Lake are respectively the fourth and fifth largest lakes on the North American continent. They are linked by the mighty Mackenzie which drains a quarter of Canada and is comparable in size to the St. Lawrence. This river system and the thousands of lakes in the Territories constitute a great food reservoir for the local residents.

Professor V. C. Wynne-Edwards, formerly of McGill University, who travelled by powered canoe a thousand miles down the Mackenzie River in 1944, wrote that the fisheries were a "staple summer industry of the Indians and of all those white residents who have to travel by dog-team during the winter." Professor Wynne-Edwards estimated that the sled dogs in the Mackenzie Valley alone consumed "several million pounds" of fish each year. Dogs are in almost every household and when working they are fed about nine pounds of raw fish every day. They snap up everything that's thrown their way—whitefish, herring and inconnu—and most of it comes from the Mackenzie River in the summer and fall when the Indians gather around the trading posts where fishing is good. The surplus catch is dried and sometimes smoked for winter use. In the fall the Indians make a special effort to catch large amounts of fish just before freeze up. This catch is frozen and provides a supply of "green" fish for the winter.

Every year in their quest for food, the Indians around Great Slave Lake and Great Bear Lake haul out several million pounds of whitefish, lake trout, inconnu and herring, as well as smaller quantities of pike and grayling. Great Bear doesn't hold much prospect for commercial fishing. Its great depth, constant cold and scarcity of bottom growth and other fish food make it naturally unproductive. Dr. R. B. Miller, of the University of Alberta, who surveyed the lake's resources for the Fisheries Research Board in 1945, found that although there were large quantities of fine lake trout in its waters, the fish populations formed merely a fringe inhabiting the near-shore zone and could not survive a large-scale commercial fishery.

Great Slave Lake, on the other hand, can support a fairly intensive commercial fishery. Several well-known western fishing companies have made it the greatest single producer of whitefish and lake trout in Canada. Ten years ago there were only some 1700 Indians and mixed-bloods and a handful of whites at the half-dozen settlements on its shores besides the three thousand or so people living at Yellowknife. Then in 1944 and 1945 Dr. D. S. Rawson, of the University of Saskatchewan, probed its depths for the Fisheries Research Board. He identified 22 different kinds of fish. As a result of his findings and recommend-ations, the Federal authorities opened the lake to commercial enterprise. The yearly quota of whitefish and lake trout set by the Department of Fisheries is nine million pounds, a figure rarely reached on account of adverse weather conditions.

Despite the fact that more than 45 million pounds of fish have been removed by the industry since 1945, there has been no appreciable effect on the fish stocks. The value of fish production ranges between one and a half and two million dollars a year, giving employment to some 500 fishermen. This operation is important in the economy of the North since the natives can work for wages both in the boats and in the filleting plants.

The opening of the all-weather highway from Grimshaw, Alta., to Hay River, a growing settlement on the south shore of the lake, has given the industry a shot in the arm. Now two or three smaller lakes in the vicinity are also fished commercially and it is believed that more of them lying within fifty miles of the major fishing grounds will be commercially fished in future seasons. At present a lack of roads limit them to winter operations. A little local trading is done in the settlements, the fresh or frozen product being sold by the "stick" which holds about 25 pounds of fish, or 10 fish strung through the gills. But the Indian can make more money trapping furs so he doesn't bother to sell fish as a regular occupation. As a result people in such places as Norman Wells and Aklavik have trouble buying what they want for their tables.

The commercial development of the fisheries for export purposes in the Northwest Territories has great possibilities. The lower Mackenzie River for instance could be commercially fished, particularly from the Sans Sault rapids north to the delta, but such a venture is not practicable yet because the catch would have to be shipped a thousand miles by refrigerator barges to Great Slave during a very

short navigable season. Freighting costs would be pro-
hibitive.

Great Slave, Great Bear and the Mackenzie River, not
to mention the thousands of other waters still untouched
by man, present exciting sport fishing possibilities. At the
present time, however, development of the resource as a
tourist attraction is confined to Great Slave Lake where two
fishing lodges have been established. One is in the east
arm of the lake at what is called Taltheilei Narrows, a
fabulous fishing ground for lake trout. For some years
before the lodge was built a few sportsmen regularly visited
this area by chartered plane. The two lodges accommodate
a limited number of the more ardent Waltonian followers
who can afford to fly from Edmonton to Yellowknife and
pay up to $100 a day for the pleasure of tangling with forty-
pound lake trout. Grayling flash their magnificent dorsal
fins along the rocky shore and at the mouths of streams,
particularly in the Yellowknife River and at Wrigley
Harbour where big ones—up to three and a half pounds—
are caught. One caught at Wrigley Harbour weighed over
four pounds—the largest on record. Sport fishing is good
around Port Radium in Great Bear. But Conjuror Bay,
South Narrows off Richardson Island, and Gunbarrel Inlet
are great places for lake trout fishing right from shore. The
grayling leap all summer in the Bear River near Fort Franklin
and in the clear waters of the Mackenzie River and its
tributaries anywhere from Providence to Arctic Red River.
Pike are generally found everywhere and often reach
extraordinary size.

The northern interiors of the provinces have rich fishery
resources which, while important as a local food supply, are
being exploited more and more by commercial and sport
fishermen. In British Columbia, the salmon runs of the
Babine, the Skeena and the Nass rivers have long been the

basis of an important canning industry. But the game fish potential of the northern interior of the province is largely unexplored. The best known game fish in these parts is the Kamloops trout. In the Babine River these fish undoubtedly provide the most excellent and most spectacular stream fishing to be found anywhere in British Columbia. The Babine is not very heavily fished by sportsmen but each year a few American parties get in and get the thrill of their lives. Other good fishing spots for Kamloops trout are Takla Lake, Cold Fish Lake in the Cassiar District and the upper reaches of the Finlay and Parsnip rivers. Arctic grayling, northern pike and lake trout are to be found in waters east of the continental divide while in the streams and coastal lakes which have access to the sea are steelhead and sea-run cutthroat trout. Undoubtedly there is a vast potential to be tapped in the northern section of the province but the inaccessibility of almost the whole area makes it unlikely that it will be exploited to any extent in the near future.

More is known about the potential of the fisheries in the northern areas of the three Prairie Provinces. Lake Athabasca, for example, yields about half a million pounds of whitefish, lake trout and other fish each year to the Chipewyan and Cree Indians and their dogs. This lake as well as others such as Lesser Slave in Alberta, and Lac La Ronge and Reindeer in Saskatchewan, have been exploited by western fishing companies since the twenties. During the war years when prices for fish were abnormally high, winter commercial operations were extended to many smaller lakes remote from rail transportation. Lake Athabasca has given up about 20 million pounds of fish since 1926 and scientists believe it could yield three times what is taken annually without showing any ill effects. Lac La Ronge has been fished since 1922 and its current commercial production is

nearly a million pounds a year.   Reindeer Lake is another
rich provider and in one year when fishing was intense,
fishermen hauled out two and one-half million pounds.   No
one knows what the lake could stand on a sustained basis
but its record over the past 14 years shows that its catch of
whitefish and lake trout represents ten per cent of the
entire production of the province of Saskatchewan.   Lesser
Slave Lake has yielded up to five million pounds of fish a
year while other northern lakes such as Wollaston, Big
Peter Pond and Ile a la Crosse each produce about half a
million pounds of fish annually.   In addition, some 63 lakes
covering an area of 80,000 square miles in northern Manitoba contribute about six million pounds of whitefish,
pickerel, pike, tullibee, trout and goldeye.   Biggest operations are in the winter when tractor trains haul the frozen
catch out to rail head points.

The authorities in the three Prairie Provinces have done
much in recent years to develop the fisheries as a tourist
attraction.   Some new regions have been opened for
automobile travel while other areas are now being well
served by train and airplane.   The Pas, which can be
reached by car, is the jumping off place for the bi-weekly
trains to Thicket Portage and Gillam and other brook trout
strongholds along the Nelson River.   The brook trout in
this river basin are famous for their size, averaging about
four pounds in weight and sometimes going as high as seven.
Other lakes abound in lake trout, while farther north, the
Owl, Deer and Churchill rivers, which flow into Hudson
Bay are the favorite heavens of the arctic grayling and the
arctic char.

In Saskatchewan, the road from Prince Albert to Lac La
Ronge was completed in 1947, bringing it within easy reach
of thousands of sports fishermen.   La Ronge had the
distinction of yielding the prize winning lake trout of 34

pounds and the biggest pike—27¾ pounds—caught in Saskatchewan's 1952 Annual Anglers' Derby. North of La
Ronge are many virgin lakes, their cold waters alive with
lake trout, northern pike and yellow pickerel or walleyes,
and of course the famous grayling. This area is accessible
at present in summer only by airplane. New sport fishing
camps are opening up at places like Cree, Wollaston, Careen
and Black Lakes. In the legendary Fond du Lac River,
linking Wollaston and Lake Athabasca, the Elizabethan
Falls at Black Lake boast the best grayling waters in the
province. As evidence of the increasing numbers of sportsmen visiting these areas, Manitoba registered some nine
thousand angling licenses issued in 1952, an increase of
more than two thousand in one year, while Saskatchewan
counted more than 44 thousand licenses issued in 1952, an
increase of nearly six thousand.

The fundamental problem in developing the fisheries of
the North is that of transportation. Dr. H. L. Keenleyside,
when he was a commissioner of the Northwest Territories,
told a group of students at McMaster University that the
whole history of the Canadian north could be divided into
two periods—before and after the airplane. This is certainly true of the fisheries. Shut off from the sportsman's
rod and the fisherman's net for many years, this almost
forgotten country had only to fulfill the needs of its native
and small white population. Today passenger and freight
planes run scheduled flights from Edmonton to Yellowknife,
to settlements of the Mackenzie valley as far north as
Aklavik and into the Yukon. The development of the
fisheries has only been possible through the airplane and
other forms of arctic transport such as the snowmobile and
diesel tractor.

There is another factor affecting the development of the
fishery resources. This is the need to protect the food

requirements of the natives.   Canada's recognition of its
social responsibility towards those who live in isolation
beyond the northern horizons forbids any enterprise which
might affect the welfare of the local population.   For
example, legislation recently enacted protects the seals,
walruses and belugas in arctic waters for native use.

The interior areas north of 55° constitute possibly the
greatest unspoiled recreation land on the continent today.
Tourist travel along the highways or by air or along the
great waterways will draw more and more people to the
great Northwest in search of new fishing thrills.   Those
who know the area believe that the game fish resources can
be maintained against any reasonable drain, particularly
when the provincial and federal authorities all are con-
servation-minded and have protection services to safeguard
the stocks.

New and important mineral finds in the North have held
the spotlight of public attention in recent years.   As a
result developments in other resources have been in the
shadows.   The fisheries, however, form an integral part of
the new foundations upon which the North's economy,
once based on fur, is now being built.   Their expansion on
such a scale that it can be regarded as a great new national
asset holds much promise.

A. Erling Porsild, M.B.E., F.R.S.C., is chief botanist at the National Museum of Canada in Ottawa. Born and educated in Denmark, he has studied the botany of Greenland and the Canadian North for many years. He is also an authority on reindeer, and was largely responsible for the importation of the herd from Alaska to the Mackenzie.

Flowers and Forests

by A. E. PORSILD

ODDLY enough some of the earliest botanical collections ever to be made in what is now Canada came from the country west of Hudson Bay, then known as Rupert's Land, part of which is now included in the present Northwest Territories. By far the most important of these were made by the naturalist and explorer, John Richardson who, between the years 1819 and 1827, accompanied Sir John Franklin's first and second overland expeditions to the shores of the Polar Sea. A great many common Canadian plants and animals, until then unknown to science and to the rest of the world, were first described from specimens collected by Richardson and by other members of the Franklin expeditions.

But it was not until 1898-1902, when a Swedish botanist accompanied the Norwegian expedition under Sverdrup, that a professional botanist visited arctic Canada; and only a quarter-century later were regular systematic botanical investigations begun under the auspices of the National Museum of Canada.

Although today more than 1400 different flowering plants and ferns are known to grow in Canada north of the 55th parallel, and no less than 834 in the Arctic alone, much is yet to be learned about plant life in the North. While there may not be many so-called "new" species yet to be discovered there, botanists are only now beginning to understand whence the plants came that repopulated the land laid waste during the last great ice age, and why some northern plants are found almost everywhere, while others which before the great ice age were more widely distributed, now have narrowly restricted ranges or strong individual preferences for particular habitats.

Even though the professional botanist may have acquired a certain amount of information about distribution and ranges of northern plants, it will probably surprise the ordinary traveller, who for the first time visits the Mackenzie delta, to see the sun hovering over the tops of tall spruce trees at midnight, on June 21. And it will probably amaze him no less to discover that beyond Aklavik the forest extends north almost to within sight of the Arctic Ocean or that, not far from Aklavik, nearly 200 miles north of the Arctic Circle, he may come across stands of white spruce measuring 100 feet in height and big enough to produce saw logs 18 to 24 inches in diameter. By way of contrast, it may be equally surprising to learn that in the vicinity of James Bay, owing to the cooling effect of that great inland sea—Hudson Bay—comparable stands of spruce are found only as far north as Moosonee. The surprise becomes even greater when he realizes that Moosonee is in approximately the same geographical latitude as London, England, more than 1000 miles (17½ degrees of latitude) south of the

Mackenzie delta. Thus, the relative distance from the geographic pole is not a reliable yardstick for climate, and latitude alone does not always provide a clue to the potential luxuriance of vegetation.

From the deck of a Mackenzie River boat we may get the impression that the great river, below Great Slave Lake, flows for more than 800 miles through densely wooded country. If, on the other hand, we travel by air we see that although the country on either side of the river is heavily wooded, the dense forest of tall trees is rather narrowly limited to the alluvial banks of the Mackenzie and its tributaries, while the low plateau through which the river has cut its valley, supports a comparatively sparse growth of trees. Away from the river valley, the trees below us become lower and more stunted. Much of the land is rocky and covered by swamps or muskegs, and before long the last trees disappear entirely to give way to a vast, treeless plain that from the air may look entirely devoid of plant life when we reach the arctic islands. But on closer inspection we see that the land which from the air looked so barren may actually support a comparatively rich plant cover. Thus, on the mainland east of the Mackenzie delta, some distance from the sea-coast, the "barrens" may for hundreds of miles be covered by heaths or moors, interspersed by countless large and small lakes. Even in the northernmost islands of the Arctic Archipelago, less than 400 miles from the North Pole, grasses, herbs and dwarf willow grow abundantly enough to furnish pasture summer and winter for herds of caribou and musk-oxen. In fact, during the short arctic summer some arctic landscapes that from the air look bleak and desolate, on close examination may appear ablaze with colour. On some south-facing slopes, watered by melt-water from a snow bank, one may even find veritable "rock gardens" gay with purple

Lapland rhododendrons and loco-weeds, yellow arctic poppies and arnicas, or creamy white avens. On cliffs or among the rocks grow masses of purple, white or yellow saxifrages, and in some rock crevices one may even detect tiny rock ferns that might well delight the most discriminating rock gardener.

Few arctic plants are of direct importance in the economy of arctic man although many are indirectly so, because they furnish food for grazing animals. Seeds, winterbuds, and the roots of many species are eaten by birds and small rodents that in turn constitute the food of some fur-bearing mammals. Likewise, the rich marine plant life indirectly furnishes food for the sea mammals so important in the economy of the Eskimo.

Only a small number of arctic plants are regularly used for food by native and white residents of the North. Not more than a few species produce edible and nourishing roots and stems, and only near the southern fringe of the Arctic are there some that regularly produce edible fruits. And yet nearly all plants, no matter where they grow, have some food value, and many, especially those that are green, are potential sources of vitamins, besides containing varying amounts of carbohydrate, protein and fat. Of greatest potential food value are the lichens, though none is used by native arctic peoples.

None of the woody species found north of the tree line are of a size large enough for constructional use by the Eskimo who, at least formerly, obtained what wood he needed chiefly from drift wood. Heather and berry bushes, stunted willows, alder and dwarf birch are all used extensively by the Eskimo for cooking purposes, but chiefly in summer. Nearly all the larger species of lichens—especially those commonly called "reindeer moss"—are highly inflammable when dry and may be used for fuel. Raw peat, particularly sod containing the roots and stems of dwarf shrubs and heather as well as partly decomposed plant remains, is available nearly everywhere in the Arctic, and in Greenland is used extensively for heating purposes.

Even though in the Arctic no land surface which is free of ice and snow in summer is entirely devoid of plant life, the number of species and the rate of growth diminishes as we approach the Pole. Everywhere plant and animal life is distributed according to definite patterns or *life zones* which are largely determined by climate. Thus, the biologist divides those two-thirds of Canada's land surface which lie north of the 55th parallel into three major life zones, each characterized by certain plants and animals found there because climatic conditions suit their requirements.

The most northern is the *Arctic Zone* which in Canada comprises approximately 900,000 square miles and includes the Arctic Archipelago and all the treeless country lying beyond the great coniferous forest belt. Samuel Hearne who, in 1770-71 was the first white traveller to explore and penetrate the arctic tundra, was so impressed by the absence of trees that he coined the phrase "barren grounds" or simply "the barrens"—a name that has remained in use even to this day.

South of the treeline, which approximately follows the 50th degree isotherm for the warmest month, the *Hudsonian Zone* extends in a roughly 200-mile-broad arc from the mouth of the Mackenzie river to the southern Labrador coast, skirting the rim of the Canadian Shield. Its southern edge roughly follows the 57th degree F. isotherm which is the northern limit of agriculture and therefore sometimes called the "crop limit."

Along mountain ridges and on high plateaus west of the Mackenzie lowlands the "barrens" extend far south into

Yukon and northern British Columbia.   The flora and fauna of this alpine country is similar to that of the Arctic zone while that of the forested foothills belong in the Hudsonian zone.

Most of the Hudsonian zone is forest-covered, but the soils are shallow, acid and poorly drained, owing to the presence of permafrost; much of the land, therefore, is swampy and the trees, which are mostly spruce, are low and stunted and of little or no commercial value.

The *Canadian Zone*, within the area north of 55°, embraces the lower parts of central and southern Yukon, the Mackenzie lowlands, northern Alberta, northeastern Saskatchewan and a narrow strip across northern Manitoba, whereas in Ontario and Quebec it does not extend north to the 55th parallel.   The Canadian Zone, too, is largely forest covered, but because the soil and climate is better, its forests are richer and more varied and of far greater economic value.

Although Alberta, Saskatchewan and Manitoba are frequently spoken of as the "Prairie Provinces," the fact remains that only one fifth of the total area of Alberta, two fifths of Saskatchewan and one sixth of Manitoba was actually prairie when first settled.   That proportion has not changed very much since, and even today practically all land north of the 55th parallel is covered by virgin forest. While the rich prairie soils near their southern fringe may always remain the most important natural resource of the Prairie Provinces, the northern and forested parts of Manitoba, Saskatchewan and Alberta together with densely forested northern half of British Columbia today possess what is undoubtedly Canada's most important untapped forest wealth.

To many of those who go to the Arctic for the first time, expecting to find nothing but ice and snow, the fact that flowers grow there at all will be amazing; and the added fact that, during the short Arctic summer, the otherwise bleak arctic tundra and rock desert may be covered by gaily coloured flowers will be the greatest wonder of all. In fact, to anyone who has spent a winter in the Arctic the experience of seeing the explosion-like progress of spring is truly an unforgettable experience; and to discover masses of Arctic flowers, where a few days ago one rode on a sled over wind-sculptured snow drifts, may seem beyond belief.

The most striking single feature in the Arctic—and the one that impressed Samuel Hearne most—is the lack of trees. To be sure there are woody plants, for even on the "barrens" far north of the tree line there are many kinds of willows and other dwarf bushes; in fact, two of them—the arctic willow and the white heather— grow as far north as land extends toward the Pole while several others do not lag far behind. But they are low, sometimes only a few inches high, and to examine them we may have to get on our hands and knees to make sure that they are really woody plants. In one tiny willow which is exceedingly common in Banks Island, the main stem is no thicker than the lead of a pencil, and moreover, is completely hidden below the surface so that only the tiny leaves and catkins emerge above the soil.

Owing to the severity of the climate and the short growing season, the rate of growth of arctic plants is very low. Most species require a period of many years before they flower and fruit for the first time. And yet, some of them may live to be very old, for wood and organic tissue roots very slowly in the Arctic where bacterial action is absent or very much reduced. Thus, the trailing stem, no thicker than a man's finger, of some arctic dwarf shrub may be several hundred years old, and only under a microscope is it possible to count the annual rings of its woody stem.

The short growing season, on the other hand, is compen-
sated for by long or continuous daylight.   True enough, the
sun is quite low, but in latitude 80° north it does not set
from April 16 to August 26, and for this reason plants growing in high latitudes enjoy more hours of sunshine than do
those of more moderate climates.   Some arctic plants are so
completely adapted to long days that when transplanted to
lower latitudes, or grown from seed there, they flower
poorly or not at all.

In the polar regions generally, but particularly in the
continental parts, precipitation is very low, often totalling
only a few inches for the year.   The winter snow-fall is
light, and frequent gales sweep the snow from the level
ground exposing the plant cover to the detrimental drying
effect of the wind and to the blast of drifting snow crystals
that at low temperatures may be as hard and sharp as grains
of sand.   So light is the rainfall during the growing season
in many parts of the Arctic, that were it not for the fact that
the soil remains permanently frozen a few inches below the
surface even in summer, thereby preventing the surface
water from penetrating beyond the reach of the plant roots,
most of the Arctic would be a lifeless desert.

And yet, while in the Arctic the vegetation is much
affected by the severe conditions under which plants grow,
the short growing season, the poor soil and low precipitation affect plant growth more adversely than the cold air.
For, due to the absorption of solar heat by the dark-coloured
soil and its vegetation, the actual micro-climate in which
the arctic plants live—that is the temperature of the surface
soil and the air surrounding the growing plant—may be
as much as 25° or even 40° F. higher than the local temperature recorded by the meteorologist's thermometer.   Here
then we have the answer to the apparent enigma: how can
plants in the Arctic germinate, produce green leaves,

flowers and fruits at air temperatures barely above 32°F.?
On sunny days, due to the absorption of solar heat, temperatures high enough for the green chlorophyl in the leaves to
convert carbon dioxide from the air into sugar and starch,
may be found near the ground or within the plant cushion
itself, even when the air temperature a few feet above
the ground may be several degrees below freezing. During
periods of unfavourable weather, the growing parts of the
plant may freeze, but are not damaged or destroyed. Thus
the effective growing season of arctic plants is prolonged
very considerably beyond the extremely short period when
freezing temperatures are not recorded by the meteorologist.

It is in adaptation to the short arctic summer, which in
some parts of the Arctic lasts barely six weeks, that almost
all truly arctic plants are perennial. The growing season is
too short for annual species to complete their life cycle in
one season. The failure of a single seed crop might spell
extinction of the species. In northern Banks Island, in the
backward season of 1949, only half a dozen species of flowering plants succeeded in maturing their seeds.

By their low and compact growth, arctic plants are well
adapted to withstand the drying effect and the mechanical
abrasion of wind and drifting sand or snow. As protection
against desiccation rather than low temperatures, the
wintering buds of many arctic plants are placed just below,
or near the surface of the ground where they are protected
by the persisting leaves of former years.

Few arctic plants depend entirely on seed production.
Vegetative propagation is widespread and takes place in a
number of ways; by adventitious buds which develop in the
leaf-axils, as in several chick-weeds and grasses, or by
stolons or runners as in the yellow saxifrage commonly
known as the "spider plant." Others have tiny bulbils
that "germinate" when detached from the mother plant

while some depend on their widely creeping rootstocks. By such means many active arctic plants are able to reproduce without seed production in much the same way in which the horticulturist propagates his rare hybrids that do not grow "true" from seed.

Thanks to their wintering buds that in many arctic species contain next year's flowering buds, a number of arctic plants require a remarkably short time to awaken from winter dormancy, come to bloom, ripen their seeds and prepare again for next winter. Thus the dainty purple saxifrage, the yellow whitlow-grass or the common arctic poppy require only one month to commence growth, flower and mature seed.

Spring comes to the Arctic with a rush. The snow disappears almost as by magic; most of it actually evaporates because the air is so dry, and before the last drifts have entirely vanished, the first flowers appear. One year at the Reindeer Depot near the mouth of the Mackenzie River, the pasque-flower or "wild crocus" (which is really an anemone), began growth on May 15 when a thin crust of snow still covered last year's withered leaves. On May 25, the large bluish-purple flowers appeared, before the silky-haired leaves had yet emerged from the ground. On June 25, the fruiting heads were fully developed, and some of the feather-tailed seeds had already been carried off by the wind.

Early in August in the Western Arctic, or a little later in the East, most plants have completed their seasonal cycle. While the seeds are maturing, new leaf- and flower-buds are formed, well-hidden among the withered leaves, and food is stored in the subterranean stems or rootstocks in readiness for next year's growth.

Terence M. Shortt is chief of the division of art and exhibits for the Royal Ontario Museum of Zoology in Toronto. Widely known through his magazine illustrations of bird life, he has made many field trips to collect bird skins in northern Canada, including a voyage on the R.M.S. Nascopie *into the Eastern Arctic.*

Wings in the Arctic

by T. M. SHORTT

So many different kinds of birds are found north of 55° that it would be impossible to deal with them interestingly in a chapter of this length. Over 300 forms inhabit the area in summer, so that in an account 3,000 words long, only ten words could be devoted, on an average, to each! It has been thought advisable, then, to limit the area under consideration to the Arctic, and furthermore to deal only with the more interesting birds of that treeless region.

The great majority of arctic birds are waterfowl—geese, ducks, swans, shorebirds, gulls and terns. And the fact that they are waterfowl means that they are mostly migratory—that with a few exceptions they stay in the Arctic only during the short season of open water. The most spectacular migrant in the world is an arctic bird, the *Arctic*

Tern, which nests as far north as land occurs and "winters" as far south as the Antarctic continent. With the exception of a brief period during their migrations while they pass through temperate and equatorial latitudes, some Arctic terns live in almost continual daylight.

But just as notable, in a different way, are the shorebirds, such as the *Plovers*, *Sandpipers* and their relatives. These are perhaps the most truly characteristic birds of the barrens. They surge into the tundra in June when break-up is well under way and tundra vegetation has come to life. The myriads of flocks streak in as if there were no time to lose. Incredible numbers swarm over every available patch of ground only recently free of snow. Immediately after their arrival the quiet tundra becomes a bedlam of activity and song as they perform their elaborate mating displays and vocal efforts. Soon nest building and egg laying are under way, and within a few weeks after the arrival, young have been hatched and are on their own while their parents are already flocking for the southward migration.

Though extreme, this routine somehow symbolizes the tempo of the arctic summer. By mid-July most of the adult birds have left the higher latitudes and some arrive on the Argentine wintering grounds in the month of August. The entire activity of summer—mating, nesting, incubating and caring for the young—has been condensed into a five or six weeks' period. But it should be remembered that the days are long and hours of activity greater than for southern birds. Though the young grow quickly, some broods are still flightless when their parents take off on their migratory journey. About one month after the exodus of the old birds the young commence their first flight south. Here, indeed, is one of the mysteries of migration. With no adult birds as pathfinders, the young travel south, some species even using a different flyway from that taken a month earlier by their parents, and arrive on schedule at the ancestral wintering grounds.

It is this extreme propensity for migration that enables such birds to penetrate into the Arctic so successfully. Most of them seldom see the winter either north or south of the equator, though some of the early arrivals in the high north come while snow is still upon the ground. By far the greater proportion of Canada's goose population nests in the Arctic—in fact the Canada goose is the only species that is not exclusively arctic. Some species are extremely local in distribution, notably *Ross's Goose*, a small, pure white bird with black wing tips and pink bill and feet. The recent discovery of the breeding grounds of Ross's goose in the vicinity of Perry River in the Central Arctic solved one of the last remaining ornithological enigmas of North America. But so few of these little geese exist that the species is in danger of extinction.

Probably the best known of the geese in the Arctic are the birds known collectively as "Waveys"*—the greater and lesser snow geese and the blue goose. *Lesser Snow Geese* are generally distributed over much of the Arctic, nesting on the low interior islands and on the northwest main coast. Coloured much like Ross's goose, they are much larger and possess a black "grinning" patch on the side of the bill. The *Greater Snow*, a still more robust bird, nests on the north-eastern islands of the archipelago. The *Blue Goose* is similar in structure to the lesser snow but has a greyish-brown body and white head. It occurs as a nesting bird principally on Baffin and Southampton Islands where it colonizes freely with the lesser snow and even interbreeds with that species. "Waveys" prefer the low, wet grassy tundras for nesting. They are important as food for the native peoples of the North. Flocks of "waveys" in flight are easily distinguished from Canada

---

* From the Cree word *wayway* .

geese by their high-pitched falsetto cries and by the flock formation. They seldom fly in a tight, firm V, but rather in irregular lines, files and crescents, and the flocks are generally large. Characteristic of the flight is a constant shifting and undulating of all or part of the flock, sometimes producing a rippling effect resembling a slow motion picture of a cracking whip.

The *Canada Goose*, largest and best known of the Canadian species, also prefers fresh water on its nesting grounds. On migration the V-shaped flocks display a tightly held formation that imparts a sense of resolution and speed and the wild barbaric music of their calls has a thrilling quality. In the Arctic there occur several populations of varying size and colour, and as yet not fully understood by ornithologists. All, however, are some shade of light brown with a black head and neck, and a white patch on the chin and cheeks. The nest is generally situated near water, and as is the case with most geese, the mated pair remain together during incubation, remaining as a family group when the young have grown up. These groups appear to stay together until migration time when a number of them may join together.

For a period after nesting season the old birds are flightless, and wander over the tundra with their young grazing on the succulent vegetation. While in this condition the flocks can be herded and captured. There still remain some aboriginal communities where life is dependent on such sources of food supply. It seems difficult to control this without imposing severe hardship or drafting laws that it would not be expedient to enforce.

It may surprise some to learn that wild swans are actually common in some localities on the arctic coast and islands west of Hudson Bay. These are *Whistling Swans*, easily recognized from all other arctic birds by their immense size, long necks and pure white plumage. Swans often arrive on the nesting grounds before the snow has melted, and linger about in the open water at the edge of the ice-pack. The nest is a huge mound-like affair, and is sometimes added to, relined and used a second year. After the nesting season, the adults, like geese, lose their power of flight through the moulting of their pinions. Most of them, however, make their way to larger bodies of water where they are relatively inaccessible.

Of the arctic ducks, most belong to the hardy salt-water groups, though a few pond ducks such as mallard, pintail and greenwinged teal do penetrate a short distance into the barren lands. The most important arctic species are the eiders and the old-squaw.

Among these, the best known is the *Common Eider*, a thoroughly maritime species, and one of the largest of ducks. The male is boldly patterned, mostly white above and black beneath, and the female is finely barred light brown and black. This is the species which provides the well-known eiderdown of commerce, though eiders in the Canadian Arctic have not yet been so successfully utilized as have those of the St. Lawrence region and of the Old World. Most of our arctic colonies, situated on rocky islands, are annually subjected to "egging" raids by the natives, and have not been afforded the kind of protection necessary to provide an eiderdown industry. The latter can only be successful when the birds are semi-domesticated and the down is harvested from their nests. Young eiders are richly clothed in soft down, and are more or less independent a short time after hatching. Though capable of looking after themselves, they often attach themselves to the nearest female with the result that an old bird is often seen with a motley brood of assorted sizes or with a humorously large number of "downies" made up of several families.

The somewhat smaller and darker *King Eider*, unlike the common species, breeds as a rule on the tundra near fresh water. It ranges along the whole northern coast and through the islands, including Ellesmere. The drake of this species displays what is undoubtedly the most striking plumage to be seen beyond the treeline. Colouring in Arctic birds is usually not brilliant. Browns and greys and muted shades of red and yellow combined with black and white are the rule. But the king eider drake sports a bizarre pattern of black and white relieved by touches of pink, pale green, and chalky blue with a fleshy hump, coloured orange-yellow and bordered with black, rising from the base of the bill.

The *Old-Squaw* is almost universal throughout the Arctic, and has been found as far north as ornithological investigations have been made. A smallish duck with small bill, parti-coloured brown and white plumage and long, pointed central tail feathers, this bird is best known for its comical, yet musical voice. The call notes of the male in spring are loud and resonant and have been rendered as *ow-ow-owdel-ow*, in chorus sounding somewhat like distant bagpipes. It is a lively restless bird with a distinctive flight, twisting and turning from side to side in the manner of a shorebird. Old-squaws have very different summer and winter colour patterns, that of summer being much darker.

The most omnipresent and conspicuous birds of the arctic summer are the gulls and terns. Some member of this family is to be found in almost every part of the polar lands or seas. The *Ivory Gull* is perhaps as truly polar as any animal. A small, almost pure white bird with black legs and yellow bill, it nests on coasts that are ice-bound until late in summer. It then ranges widely over the ice-pack in search of food. Its distribution is controlled to a large extent by the annual routine of seals, walrus and polar bear, for it is a scavenger, and obtains much of its sustenance from the droppings of these animals.

There are enormous colonies of other gulls on suitable cliffs and ledges throughout the rugged portions of the arctic land masses. These gulls—Thayer's, herring, glaucous and kittiwakes—derive most of their food from the sea. Inland, Sabine's gull and the arctic tern frequent the edges of grassy tundra pools and gravel or sand bars during the nesting season.

Related to the gulls, and exclusively arctic, are the three species of *Jaegers*—pomarine, parasitic and long-tailed. These are fierce hawk-like birds with webbed and clawed feet and long, hooked bills. Of graceful flight, jaegers may be distinguished from hawks and gulls by their long central tail feathers. They are truly birds of prey, capturing, often in flight, small shorebirds and songbirds, and varying their diet with offal, small mammals and fish. The latter they obtain largely by pursuing terns and forcing them to drop the fishes they have caught.

All of the world's four species of *Loon* are found in the Arctic. Two, the yellow-billed and arctic loons are exclusively tundra-nesting species, the red-throated almost entirely so, while the common loon, so familiar to summer cottagers in the northern evergreen forest, penetrates the Arctic to Baffin Island and beyond tree-limit in the western mainland. The two common species throughout most of the Arctic are the red-throat and the arctic. The cries of these birds are as weird and as characteristic of the tundra pools as are those of their big relative of the clear, conifer-rimmed lakes farther south. Both species nest at the edges of snow pools and small lakes, usually within a few miles of the sea or larger bodies of fresh water in which aquatic animal life is available for food. The sight of low-

flying loons on their excursions from their nests to the feeding grounds and back, is well known to those who have
camped on the tundra.   The nest is located so that access
to it can be achieved directly from the water, for loons are
virtually helpless on land.   When the two young hatch
from the large olive-brown eggs, they take to the water as
soon as they are dry.   They are clad in dense, dark down
and float buoyantly like corks.   Both parents tend and
guard them devotedly for a long period, and even after the
young are able to fly, the family group may stay together
for some time.

The greater part of the barrens is uninviting to birds,
but on the grass tundra lands, bird life is abundant during
the short summer.   Such areas are flat, have good plant
cover, and are dotted and laced with snow pools, lakes and
waterways.   They are generally near sea-level, and were
below it in recent geological times.   There is adequate
cover for nesting and a plentiful food supply.   In some such
areas, teeming with sandpipers, plovers, terns, ducks and
geese, ptarmigan, loons and songbirds, the population of
birds per acre is likely to approach that of more favoured
localities in the wooded parts of Canada.

But as the short summer wanes, and the great migratory
exodus gets under way, even the grass tundra areas, which
for a few weeks of almost perpetual daylight have supported
this large bird population, are soon engulfed in the long dark
winter during which they are almost devoid of birds.   A
few ravens, ptarmigan, and snowy owls are all that are left.

These land birds, however, who brave the bitter Arctic
winter, are among the most interesting of the region.   The
ptarmigan moults into white livery for the months of snow,
and like the snowy owl is equipped with a heavy growth
of soft feathers on the legs and toes.   The raven, however,
keeps his black coat the year round, and goes through the

far northern winter with his legs and toes completely naked.

The *Ptarmigan* is unique among birds in having a seasonal change of concealingly coloured plumage. In winter they are white except for the black tail—which is usually hidden—and black shoe-button eyes. The summer dress is a mixture of buff, russet and black, beautifully designed for tundra camouflage. There are two species of this bird in the Canadian Arctic—the willow ptarmigan, a bird of the grassy tundras, and the rock ptarmigan, a smaller, greyer bird of more northern distribution which is adapted to a more rocky and mountainous environment. In spring the landscape is enlivened by the display of the males, as they go through their mating behaviour. White wings flashing, brilliant red combs extended, they strut, run, perform aerial gyrations and crow from every elevation— boulder or dune. On the nest the female is perfectly concealed by her pattern and colour, and will often remain on the eggs until touched or stepped upon. The young are heavily clothed in soft down, even to their toes, and are capable of running an hour or so after hatching. They can fly when ten days old. Like the snowy owl, ptarmigan are subject to cyclic fluctuations in numbers, and in peak years emigrate in vast numbers, flying and walking as far south as settled communities of southern Canada.

Of the owls, the great *Snowy Owl* is the only one regularly occurring beyond the tree limit. Pure white, or barred with brown, and equipped with powerful talons concealed in long fluffy feathers, the snowy is to be found in summer from the tree line north as far as the land is capable of supporting the small mammals and birds on which it subsists. The snowy makes its nest on the ground of the open tundra, and there is an interval between the laying of each of the six to eight eggs. Incubation commences as soon as the first is laid, and the young hatch about two days apart. When the last egg hatches, the eldest young, clothed in soft, grey down, may be two weeks old! Periodically the snowy owl builds up to a peak population which seems to pass the "living space" saturation point. In such winters a great mass emigration takes place. Owls pour down over settled Canada and the northern United States where most of them perish, many at the hands of man, and few live to return to their arctic home.

Of the other land birds of prey, the most characteristic arctic hawk is the *Gyrfalcon*, largest and most robust of the world's falcons. It nests on cliffs or on elevations in the open tundra, and shows a remarkable colour variation from almost pure white to almost black. These colour variants have nothing to do with age or sex, but seem to have some geographic significance. The white form is found on the islands of the far north. Despite their reputations among falconers for great speed and strength, gyrfalcons lack the dash and spirit of the peregrine, and while they frequently do take large birds as food, they seem to prefer to hunt lemmings and small birds. Gyrfalcons use the same nesting site year after year, and excrement and remnants from meals (bones, fur and feathers) may pile up until they form a large whitish mass visible from far away.

Along the wild, rugged coasts where myriads of sea-birds congregate, will be found the *Peregrine*, the swiftest and most aggressive of all birds. Its flight is characteristically direct and rapid, progressing by a series of fast, winnowing beats and long glides, or when covering long distances by deep, steady wing beats. It feeds almost entirely on other birds, in the Arctic preferring murres, guillemots and shorebirds. These are taken by direct pursuit of flying quarry, which is struck down in mid-air by a tremendous punch of the closed foot, or seized in the powerful talons. The peregrine has been observed to overtake some of the swiftest sandpipers and plovers on the wing, and when in playful mood even large insects are captured thus. The richly coloured red-brown eggs are laid on a bare rock ledge usually on the face of a sheer cliff. The parent birds are noisy about the nest, uttering a harsh "kak-kak-kak" when disturbed.

In contrast the big, sluggish *Rough-legged Hawk* seems almost lazy and gentle. It is essentially a small-mammal eater, lemmings forming the bulk of its diet in the Arctic. Often it is seen hovering in one spot, with just enough wing action to keep it aloft until it sights its prey, when it drops swiftly on the unsuspecting rodent. It nests on cliff ledges, on high banks or on the ground in the open tundra.

Birds classified as "song-birds" are poorly represented in the Arctic in number of species, but the few kinds which do occur are very abundant. Many nest as far north as tree-limit, and even a short distance beyond where stunted spruce and willow and dwarf birch dot the tundra, but a mere half dozen or so can be said to be typical birds of the treeless regions. The *Horned Lark*, well known on the prairies and in the cleared lands of the east, is represented in the north by larger forms that are found in some of the bleakest and most rugged areas of desert tundra. The little *Pipit* ranges far and wide, and is found north to the Arctic Sea and southern Baffin Island. The commonest of the small sparrow-like birds, however, are the *Snow-Bunting* and the *Lapland Longspur*. Both species have been found on Ellesmere Island. Both are tundra nesters, and build beautiful nests on the ground, usually warmly lined with ptarmigan feathers.

The *Raven* is one of the most remarkably successful of arctic birds, and is to be found wherever there is land. Its success in populating polar regions lies in its ability to adjust itself to almost any food supply, animal or vegetable. It has a strong partiality to the former and prefers the coastal regions, where in season it can secure the offal of the sea, carcasses of whales, seals, fishes and marine inverte-brates, and conduct raids on the sea-bird colonies for eggs and young birds. It is also capable of catching lemmings and subsisting on berries and other plant matter.

Much of the continental land area north of 55° is covered by the great coniferous forest, where a bird fauna richer than that of the treeless arctic is to be found. Perch-ing birds, so scarce on the tundra, are abundant in the forest, and many kinds, such as the robin, flicker, kingbird and song sparrow, which are familiar about farm and orchard in the south, are equally at home in these latitudes. In addition there are several species that are peculiar to the coniferous forest, such as the crossbills, Canada jay, olive-backed thrush, pigeon hawk, brown-headed chickadee and spruce grouse.

The fringe belt of muskeg and scattered shrubby trees supports some of the hardiest of tree-nesting birds. Species like redpoll, grey-cheeked thrush, black poll warbler and tree, fox and white-crowned sparrows undoubtedly could survive the climate and would occur much farther north were it not for the absence of their traditional nesting sites, either in or protected by trees.

Much has yet to be learned about the distribution and habits of northern birds, and the amateur can make a useful contribution. Observations of the occurrence of even the commonest species, especially in high polar regions, are welcomed by ornithologists as additional facts that help to explain puzzling problems of bird distribution.

Muskeg near Mackenzie delta with tussocks of cotton grass.   A.E.P.

Pasque flowers (anemones) appear in the Mackenzie delta with the first
touch of spring.   A.E.P.

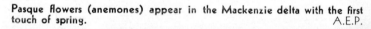

Creeping arctic willow grows as far north as land reaches toward the Pole, and furnishes the bulk of the food of musk oxen. A.E.P.

Cushions of moss pink brighten the arctic landscape. A.E.P.

Bearded winter wheat at Dominion Experimental Station, Mile 1016 on the
Alaska Highway.

Arctic Loons.

Peregrine Falcon launching in pursuit of Murres.

Parasitic Jaeger robbing Long-Tailed Jaeger of its prey.

King Eider drakes.

drawings by Terence M. Shortt

King-size cabbages are grown at Aklavik, where midsummer days are 24 hours long.   Geo. Hunter

Experimental farm of the Department of Agriculture, at Fort Simpson on the Mackenzie River.   Geo. Hunter

Folded strata in the northern Arctic folded belt.   National Museum

Oil storage tanks at Norman Wells on the Mackenzie.   Geo. Hunter

Dr. A. H. Lang, Geological Survey of Canada, detects the presence of uranium with a Geiger counter.

Geo. Hunter

A stoping machine in operation in a gold mine.

Geo. Hunter

Grant MacEwan, M.Sc., formerly Dean of Agriculture at the University of Manitoba and a director of the Royal Bank of Canada, is now manager of the Council of Canadian Beef Producers. Active in public affairs—he is an alderman of the city of Calgary and president of various clubs and associations—he has seen seven of his books published, among them Between the Red and the Rockies, Sodbusters, *and* Agriculture on Parade.

Food from the Soil

by GRANT MacEWAN

MISUNDERSTANDING and prejudice are inherited handicaps that Canada's northern soil has had to overcome. The winters were too cold; the summers were too short; the permafrost was too close to the surface to permit the successful production of domestic plants and animals, and the area was too isolated—or so the reasoning seemed to run.

Those illusions were not unlike the clouds of fear that once plagued the good farming country lying across the southern part of the western provinces. Even at the middle of last century Sir George Simpson, who had experienced many years in the West, could see no future for agriculture to the westward from Red River. At that period, our Great Plains that today are among the world's major spring wheat producers, were seen as an area in which nobody would care to build a home. Little more than a generation ago, Sam Livingstone was mildly criticized for trying to grow wheat close to the present city of Calgary, and people laughed at A. P. Stevenson for attempting to grow apples in southern Manitoba.

Gradually Canadians learned the truth concerning the high productivity of prairie and park belt soils in their western provinces but tended to cling to the "land of ice and snow" concept about areas farther north. The unknown can be counted on to breed superstitions. With 50 per cent of Canada's population living within 100 miles of the International Boundary, and 90 per cent within 200 miles of it, large tracts in the north continued to be unoccupied and unappreciated. But the fact was that Aklavik, at the mouth of the Mackenzie River and some 1600 miles north of Pincher Creek, Alberta, was on Canadian soil and had considerable native vegetation that would not be unfamiliar to Canadians living in the southern belt.

Even after the beginning of the present century, well-meaning teachers, seeking to test youthful memories, asked Grade VIII pupils to sketch on maps of the mid-West, the "northern limits of cultivation." Obedient youngsters (of whom the MacEwan boy was one) would project pencil marks through points marked "Dauphin," "Prince Albert" and "Edmonton." Grade eighters were ready to accept the implied conclusion that no normal and self-respecting domesticated seeds which were dropped in the "frigid soil" beyond that line, could be expected to germinate or grow.

Even today, there is much hand-me-down prejudice about the "frozen north," and in fairness to the only remaining agricultural frontier, back of which is about 50 per cent of Canada's surface, the nation's citizens have to revise their thinking. Clearly, those who are most familiar with the North, show the least concern about long winters, the permafrost and the diminishing isolation.

Furs drew the first white people to the north, but something else was needed to support more than the sparsest population. The other resources were there, however, and when the search for new wealth went underground, one source of wealth after another was discovered. The northern parts of the provinces gave up their secrets about gold at Goldfields, copper, zinc and silver at Flin Flon, salt at Waterways, uranium at Uranium City, fish in a thousand lakes, water power on the rivers, and forest products across the country.

Farther north, in the Yukon and the Northwest Territories, there is the same strong case for a new deal. Exploration and development are in the air. The new roads, the new railways and the new network of air routes, have reduced northern isolation.

Now, exploration and mining development ensure increased population. Northern appetites are big ones and immediately the question arises about the suitability of climate and soil for agriculture and the north's capacity for food production. Northern agriculture can best serve growing industry by providing fresh foods to supplant the canned products being shipped in at high cost.

Wherever there is soil, the north can produce food products. Failure to recognize this could seriously retard general development. To build up the hope of an agricultural kingdom, such as the southern prairies and park belt now know, would be equally unfortunate and wrong. There will be distinct limitations to northern farm development, but such will be imposed by lack or absence of soil over much of the Canadian Shield, more than by climatic severities.

Agriculture knows no substitute for soil. But where there is acceptable soil in the north, there will be cultivation, ultimately.

Unfortunately, the northern soils are not adequately mapped, and until more work has been done to mark and assess the existing areas of useful types, agricultural possibilities will be uncertain. But having regard to the fact that agriculture can flourish only where there is soil, the chief opportunities north of latitude 55° will be in the Northwest rather than on the northern part of the Labrador Peninsula. Hence, for purposes of this chapter, the northern sections of the four western provinces, along with the Northwest Territories and Yukon, will receive the most attention.

What areas offer the best chance for agricultural development? Unfortunately that question cannot be answered with any degree of conclusiveness. Speaking of those areas about which soil information is available, northern sections of Manitoba, Saskatchewan, Alberta and British Columbia will certainly witness a continued expansion of farming. Impressive areas of clay soils west of The Pas and north of the Hudson Bay Railroad will attract settlement, and each of the other western provinces, including British Columbia with inter-mountain valleys like the Parsnip-Finlay Valley, has productive frontier districts. In the Peace River area of Alberta, several million acres of agricultural land may yet be thrown open for settlement.

Farther north, in the Yukon and the Northwest Territories, there are acres of promising farm land along the numerous rivers and lakes. Northern soil is variable and not all of it is good by present-day standards. Some of those northern soils are covered with muskeg and poorly drained, and some are of the grey wooded type and so badly leached that they have doubtful value for agriculture. But that emphasizes more than ever the utter necessity of the soil survey as a forerunner of settlement.

It seems a reasonable guess, however, that the Yukon will have at least half a million acres useful for farming, and probably a million. The Northwest Territories with the Mackenzie River valley running through them, will have a good deal more of promising agricultural soil; it is thought that the valleys of the Mackenzie, Slave, Hay and Liard Rivers alone will furnish more than a million acres suitable for agriculture.

As the Council of the Northwest Territories met in 1953, one of the first matters to come under discussion was a proposal to make available for market gardening, 22,000 acres of land within ten miles of Hay River, on Great Slave Lake, 500 miles north of Edmonton; and W. D. Albright, who was superintendent of the Federal Government experimental station at Beaverlodge from 1919 to 1945, and is one well informed about the North, argued that the valley of the Liard River has an agricultural destiny which may one day rival that of Peace River. The new north will never be able to show expanses of rich soil as vast as those of Regina Plains or Carrot River; the northern soils will be patchy and some areas of good soil may seem small when compared with the older districts; but nothing seems more certain than that the good soils will be needed, wherever they are.

Domestic plantings on a small scale were conducted at northern trading posts like York Factory, Fort Dunvegan and Fort Simpson over a hundred years ago. But the public took small notice and the experiments had to be conducted over and over again. It was too quickly forgotten that one of the first samples of wheat to win an international championship for Canada was grown between Dunvegan and Peace River Crossing. That was in 1893 and the grower was Rev. J. G. Brick who went to Dunvegan as a missionary, about 12 years earlier. He grew his prize wheat about 450 miles north of the International Boundary.

Still closer to the northern boundary of Alberta is Fort Vermilion which boasts an agricultural record that will bear study.   To that section went Sheridan Lawrence with his parents in 1886 and there he remained to make an out-standing success operating on a thousand acres and running a herd of 200 to 300 cattle.

When the Lawrences went in, there was no railroad north of Calgary and not even a respectable trail north of Edmonton.   From Calgary, it was a 900-mile journey. But the land that was considered to be so far back com-pletely won Lawrence's loyalty and confidence.   Since 1907, the Experimental Farms Service has conducted experi-mental work there at Fort Vermilion, growing about as wide a range of cereals, forages, fruits (including hardy apples) and ornamentals as would be found on a prairie station.

The agricultural triumphs of the Peace River country, on the British Columbia side as well as on the Alberta side, are now fairly well known.   However much or little out-siders know about Peace River, there is no place in Canada where one will encounter more local enthusiasm about the qualities of soil, scenery and climate.   One may encounter fields of winter wheat near Grande Prairie in township 71 and outstanding crops of alfalfa at Manning in township 91, some fifty miles north of Peace River town.   Signboards at the entrance to the towns of Sexsmith and Dawson Creek tell the visitor that here is the "Grain Capital" of the Empire in one case and "Largest Grain Shipping Centre" in the Empire, in the other.   And if the visitor goes on to Grimshaw, he may hear that the town's grain-shipping record surpasses that of both neighbors!

In seed grain prizes and championships, it would seem that Grande Prairie district in the Peace River area has a record not to be rivalled anywhere. Robert Cochrane, who drove a pair of horses over the Klondike Trail from Edmonton and reached Peace River with the first wave of settlers in 1910, may have led the seed grain championship parade. He won the timothy seed championships at Chicago in 1932 and at the World's Grain Show at Regina in 1933. At the same world show at Regina, Cochrane was among the winners with Kharkov winter wheat.

To recount the international winnings with seed grain from that Grande Prairie area is to recall the striking series of wheat crowns won by Herman Trelle. Five times he secured the world championship for his district of Wembley, just a few miles west of the town of Grande Prairie. Various other growers in that area had one or two international championships with wheat and other cereals, and not far from the Trelle farm was Percy Clubine, an international winner with seed peas, who preferred to talk about his struggles on the Edson Trail when he drove into the district and homesteaded in 1911.

North in the Territories and the Yukon, farming has never flourished. Cultivation to help meet local food needs was stimulated by the Klondike gold rush in 1898, but the interest was of brief duration. In 1941, the total farm land in the Yukon was 2781 acres on 26 farms, of which only 1050 acres were actually in crop to cereals, grass, alfalfa and potatoes. Ten years later, the census showed a decline rather than expansion, the cultivated acreage in 1951 being recorded as 80 acres on a total of four farms. The two sets of figures are misleading, because of a difference in method of reporting. The obvious conclusion, however, is that active farming in the latter year was negligible.

The Federal Department of Agriculture inaugurated a program of co-operative experiments in 1915, and between 1917 and 1925 an experimental substation was operated six miles from Dawson. In most years the crops were good, although early frost caused loss on some occasions. In 1943, the Experimental Farm Service revived its program for that northern area and one of its first tasks was a reconnaissance survey of soils along the Alaska Highway and in the Yukon River basin. A new site for an experimental substation was chosen about a hundred miles west of Whitehorse; its location is beside the highway, in the western part of Dezadeash Valley where, it was expected, there would be more than a hundred thousand acres of agricultural land. With the likelihood of another sixty thousand useful acres along the Yukon River, the need for experimentation appeared obvious.

That Whitehorse substation at Mile 1019 on the Alaska Highway had 105 acres of cleared land for experimental work in 1953. Right at the historic site of Whitehorse there is not much good soil and hence even gardens are not very common; but Dawson has been quite successful and has won a reputation for good tomatoes and potatoes.

In the Territories where total cultivated acreage in 1950 was estimated at not more than 2000 acres, potatoes and vegetables have been first in importance. At Fort Simpson, where there have been small scale plantings since early fur-trade years, there has been an experimental substation since 1946, and in 1953 it had 50 acres cleared for cropping. Probably the best established individually owned farms in the Territories are beside the Mackenzie River, close to Fort Simpson.

At new and fabulous Yellowknife, in latitude 62° and 640 air miles from Edmonton, the main handicap to growing domestic crops is lack of suitable soil—sand, clay and muskeg being the prevalent types. But on the better soils of the district, vegetable production is being conducted successfully to meet the needs of a rapidly growing population.   C. C. Bevan, C. O. Callaghan and Martin Bode, with 19 acres of vegetables between them in 1948, were doing a pioneer service with seeds and were marketing fresh vege-tables in mid-June when the frostline in some places was not much more than a foot below the surface.

A journey down the Mackenzie River to its mouth on the Arctic coast would demonstrate clearly that mosquitoes thrive and flowers bloom along that north-country lifeline, as elsewhere, and that the Mackenzie Valley has consider-able soil which would furnish a wide variety of food pro-ducts in return for reasonable effort.   When I visited quaint little Aklavik at the Mackenzie mouth in June 1948, Bruno Weidman's garden crops and oats were a little better than many seen in Saskatchewan in the same season.

At Norman Wells on the Mackenzie River, about 800 miles from Edmonton and only 55 miles south of the Arctic Circle, some experimental plantings have served to confirm the practicability of cropping for local requirements.   The loam and muck soils there may require drainage and they may need extra phosphorous or something else, but they are black and rich and high in organic matter.   With 22 different varieties planted on less than an acre in the first experimental year, nearly 7500 pounds of vegetables were harvested.

In the next year, 1949, with a little larger plant and the application of some 9-27-9 fertilizer, the harvest of 12,000 pounds of vegetables was considered a still better crop. The experimental plantings of that year included Saunders wheat, Ajax oats and Olli barley, all of which came to maturity with good acreage yields.   So encouraging were those Norman Wells experiments (conducted with the co-operation of the Imperial Oil Company officials there) that in the next year bush fruits, cherries, plums and crabapples were shipped north and planted in the deep black soil beside the Mackenzie, close to the land of Midnight Sun. For the first couple of years, at least, the fruit trees and shrubs did well and there seemed to be every probability that their survival would continue.

How is it that the vegetables and cereals can mature in these northern areas where winters are severe and summers short? In the first place, the severity of the winter may not have so much to do with it and anyway, northern winters are not so much colder than Winnipeg and Edmonton winters as many people suppose. The Canadian-born explorer Stefansson, who spent many winters and summers in the far north, has said that he found the cold and storms of North Dakota winters more unpleasant than those on the Arctic Coast. Partly, the explanation lies in the fact that from a cold centre in the Yukon, the winter climate seems to moderate as one approaches the Arctic Ocean.

Summer climate certainly is a factor in agriculture but northern summers, though relatively short, are generally favorable. Rainfall is not heavy as a rule; surprising as it may seem to many Canadians, the average annual precipitation at Fort Vermilion in Northern Alberta, Fort Simpson deep in the Territories, Norman Wells farther north and Dawson in the Yukon, would be no more than the average for Medicine Hat, Alberta, but north country evaporation is lighter and thus the north is more economical with its moisture.

The most striking feature about cultural conditions in the north is the rapidity of growth, due to long hours of sunlight. Dawson may expect about 80 consecutive frost-free days in a summer season, Norman Wells about 85, and Aklavik about 65. Such periods are short compared to frost-free days farther south, but longer hours of sunlight make an effective compensation. Plant physiologists explain that photosynthesis in the leaves of the plants is directly related to the intensity and duration of sunlight. Instead of talking about "consecutive frost-free days," it might be better if we could use the number of hours of sunlight in the frost-free period as a basis in making comparisons.

Only those who have witnessed the rate of plant growth in the land of the midnight sun or at Norman Wells where there will be 22 hours of sunlight a day for most of June, can appreciate it. V. J. Love who is in charge of the experimental substation at Fort Vermilion close to the northern boundary of Alberta, has pointed out that Thatcher wheat grown at that point matured in 32 fewer days than the same variety at Lacombe over 400 miles farther south while Victory oats at Fort Vermilion matured in 19 fewer days than at Beaverlodge and nearly 26 fewer days than at Lacombe. Thus it will be seen that Fort Vermilion with an average of 72 frost-free days per year, can mature almost any annual crop that would grow successfully at Lethbridge, Alberta, where the average for frost-free days is 116.

Those interested in northern cultivation will find special interest in the climatologist's conclusion that the northern hemisphere is in a period of rising temperatures. Even Western Canada's weather records for a period of fifty years show a gradual rise in mean temperatures. If temperatures continue to rise over a long period, major agricultural changes would be inevitable and the North would feel it more than the southerly areas. One disadvantage of higher temperatures would be an increase in the rate of evaporation with increased drought hazard as a result.

Domestic livestock have followed the settlers into the farming districts in northern Manitoba, Saskatchewan, Alberta and British Columbia, and no one questions the appropriateness of producing beef, pork, mutton, dairy products, poultry and eggs in these areas. Farmers in those sections have not gone to extreme lengths in mechanization and consequently the horse population in Peace River area will be higher than in a representative prairie district.

It may be significant that Peace River has not made as much headway with other livestock as in field crops. But livestock improvement is on the way, and Fairview, in Peace River, held its first public sale of pure bred bulls in the spring of 1953. Outstanding herd sires such as the shorthorn, Killearn Max Juggler, brought to Fairview in the spring of 1952 at a cost of $4400, will have an important influence upon the commercial livestock to be shipped out in the years ahead.

Some of Canada's most rugged and most northerly cattle ranches are west of the Alaska Highway, in districts served by Dawson Creek and Fort St. John. One of the pioneers in that cattle country was J. R. Ardill, who in 1920 located on the north side of Peace River, not far from Hudson's Hope, B.C. His foundation in that year was a single cow with bull calf at foot, brought in from Edmonton via Peace River Crossing and delivered at the new ranch by river boat. From that little cow, through successive generations of offspring, came the entire herd of about 300 Hereford cattle being carried on the ranch in 1953. The 800 acres of Ardill crop land, the excellent crops of alfalfa for fodder and for seed, and the good cattle turned off each year are excellent testimony for that township.

North of the southern boundary of the Territories and the Yukon, the native livestock must far outnumber the domestic kinds. The census of 1951 gave the Yukon a domestic livestock population of 15 cattle and five horses, which represented a decline from 1941.

When C. C. Bevan airlifted six Holstein cows and a thousand hens to the upstart town of Yellowknife it appeared as a big gamble, and friends insisted that the hens would be a failure in that latitude. But instead of being discouraged or overcome by the long winter and hours of darkness, the Bevan hens laid at a rate that would have seemed progressive in any part of agricultural Canada.

At first the Bevan cows had to live on hay that was brought in by air, some costing as much as $175 a ton, so that a price of 55 cents a quart on fresh milk sold to cus- tomers in the mining town didn't seem too much. It all served to demonstrate the need for a northern agriculture that would provide home grown feeds for animals and the fresh foods so necessary in proper human nutrition.

Aklavik in 1948 had one cow. There was no other member of her species for hundreds of miles in any direction and at most centres in the far north there were no domestic animals except dogs. There is no reason to suppose, how- ever, that, when feed can be produced and shelter provided, the domestic livestock will not thrive.

Domestic meat-producing animals may be scarce or absent over much of the North but the wild species offering meat foods capable of human use are impressive enough. Wood buffalo occupying land on both sides of Alberta's northern boundary, have multiplied and flourished. The reindeer driven from Alaska and introduced to an area east of the Mackenzie River Delta have likewise multiplied; 2370 head were delivered in 1935 after an eventful drive extending over six years, and in 1950, there were 7000 head that would serve as an effective aid in furnishing food for Eskimos and others along the Arctic coast.

In the final analysis, the extent of northern agriculture will bear a direct relationship to the amount of good soil that can be found. In the interests of national defence, expanding industry and agriculture itself, it would be well if a more systematic survey of northern soils were pursued without delay.

Frederick J. Alcock, Ph.D., F.R.S.C., has been chief curator of the National Museum of Canada for seven years. A graduate in geology of Toronto and Yale, he served with the Geological Survey of Canada from 1915 to 1947. Among his special areas of investigation were the northern parts of Manitoba and Saskatchewan.

Wealth from the Rocks

by F. J. ALCOCK

THE mineral deposits of Canada north of fifty-five are probably that region's greatest potential source of wealth. In spite of the long distances from important commercial centres, production has taken place in a number of areas in the past and is being carried on at the present time, and the current increasing activity in geological mapping and prospecting will undoubtedly lead to new discoveries. In this connection, photographs of the country taken from the air are of paramount importance. The use of the aeroplane too, particularly on the lake-dotted Canadian Shield, has revolutionized travel and transportation, making it possible to cover in a matter of hours distances which formerly took weeks by canoe.

This region north of the 55th parallel includes parts of three of the five major geological divisions into which the

entire country naturally falls, and also the whole of one
other of these divisions. The fifth, the Appalachian region
of eastern Canada, lies completely south of that parallel.
The three divisions partly included are the Canadian Shield,
the Interior Plains, and the Cordilleran region. The one
lying wholly within the area under discussion is known as
the Northern Arctic folded belt. Each of these has its
own particular type of topography, geology, and minerals.

The Canadian Shield[1] is a vast V-shaped area with an
arm on either side of Hudson Bay. Its total area is about
1,825,000 square miles of which considerably more than
half lies north of fifty-five. Topographically it is mainly a
region of low relief, hummocky topography, and highly
disorganized drainage.[2] It is the great lake region of the
world, containing more lakes than all of the rest of the
world together, lakes of all sizes, with very irregular shore-
lines and commonly containing many islands, while the river
stretches connecting them are marked by rapids and water-
falls. These drainage features and the rounded and
smoothed forms which the outcrops of rock show are the
result of deposition and erosion by ice when, during the
Pleistocene or Glacial epoch (see Geological Time Chart),
continental glaciers occupied the region.

The rocks of the Shield are all of Precambrian age and
are therefore very ancient—about two billion to 500 million
years old. During this age, mountain-building took place
repeatedly, accompanied by folding and faulting (fracturing)
of the strata and by the intrusion of igneous masses—that is,
rocks formed by the cooling of material which was once in a
molten state. These were the occasions when mineralization took place, with the formation of ore deposits.

In late Precambrian time, this uplifted region was eroded
to one of low relief by rain, wind, frost, streams, and so on,
and during the subsequent Palaeozoic era (500 million to 200

1. So named by the famous Austrian geologist, Suess, chiefly because of its shape, but partly because it is
the strong, unyielding part of the country, which has not suffered folding nor mountain-building since very early
time, and is therefore like a shield or buckler.

2. E.g. Wollaston Lake, in northeastern Saskatchewan, drains two ways—into Hudson Bay through Reindeer Lake and the Churchill River, and into the Polar Sea through Lake Athabasca and the Mackenzie River.

GEOLOGICAL TIME CHART

ERA	PERIOD	CHARACTERISTIC LIFE	Total estimated time in years.
CENOZOIC	Recent / Pleistocene	Man	
			1,000,000.
	TERTIARY: Pliocene / Miocene / Oligocene / Eocene / Paleocene	Mammals and modern plants	
			60,000,000.
MESOZOIC	Cretaceous / Jurassic / Triassic	Reptiles and gymnosperms	
			200,000,000.
PALÆOZOIC	Permian / Carboniferous: Pennsylvanian / Mississippian / Devonian / Silurian / Ordovician / Cambrian	Amphibians and lycopods / Fishes / Higher invertebrates	
			500,000,000.
PRECAMBRIAN — Proterozoic	Keweenawan / Huronian	Primitive invertebrates and algae	
			1,100,000,000.
PRECAMBRIAN — Archæan	Timiskaming / Keewatin	Nil	
			2,000,000,000.

π53

million years ago) and the Mesozoic era (200 million to 60 million years ago) seas advanced over parts of it and later retreated. In the still later Cenozoic era (60 million years ago to the present) much of the sedimentary rock which had been deposited in these seas was removed by erosion; and finally at the close of that era, during the Pleistocene period, glaciers of continental extent modified the topography and thoroughly disorganized the drainage.

The types of ore deposits that might be expected to occur, and do occur, in such a region are primary ores of the metals such as gold, silver, copper, iron, lead, zinc, uraninite, etc., materials given off as vapors and solutions by intrusive igneous rocks in the later stages of their cooling. Placer deposits such as are formed in the Yukon are hardly to be expected, since glacial erosion by the Pleistocene ice-sheets tended to remove any accumulated gravels. Deposits of coal, oil, or gas are also not to be expected, for such occurrences are associated with beds of younger strata, containing fossils, the Precambrian rocks only extremely rarely showing any evidence of organic life having existed when they were formed. The gold deposits of the Porcupine and Kirkland Lake areas of Ontario, the copper-gold ores of Quebec, and silver of Cobalt, the nickel-copper of Sudbury, the iron of Steep Rock and Quebec-Labrador, and the gold-copper-zinc of Flin Flon are but a few examples of the tremendous wealth already developed in the Shield south of fifty-five, and are an indication of what may be expected to be found north of that parallel.

The Interior Plains region lies mainly to the west of the Canadian Shield. It is characterized by fairly level or rolling topography and geologically it is underlain by flat-lying or only gently dipping rocks of Palaeozoic, Mesozoic, and Cenozoic age. There are also a number of smaller, separated, similar areas which are spoken of as outliers of

the Interior Plains.   Such a one underlain by flat Palaeozoic
sediments borders the west coast of Hudson and James Bays.
Others occur on many of the Arctic islands where lowlands
are underlain by Palaeozoic and younger strata resting on
Precambrian rocks of the Canadian Shield.

The mineral deposits of this division include petroleum,
coal (of Cretaceous and Tertiary age), natural gas, bituminous sands, gypsum, etc.   Zinc and lead also occur in
Devonian beds southwest of Great Slave Lake.

The Cordilleran Region includes the mountainous country to the west of the Interior Plains.   It is a region
marked topographically by high relief, and geologically by
rocks ranging in age all the way from Precambrian to Recent.
Over 90 million years ago the region suffered folding, and
the intrusion on a large scale of masses of granite.   These
were the sources of extensive mineralization of gold, copper,
silver, lead, zinc, iron and other metals.   A later period of
deformation took place over 60 million years ago and continued for some millions of years.   It was at this time that
the Rocky Mountains were built.

This region, in addition to deposits of metals, contains
coal, petroleum, natural gas, and gypsum.

The Northern Arctic Folded Belt includes many of the
islands in the northern part of the Arctic archipelago.   It
extends from the northeast end of Ellesmere Island immediately west of the upper part of Greenland in a southwest direction for 800 miles.   It is a region of folded
Palaeozoic and Mesozoic rocks, and it includes mountains
which on Ellesmere reach elevations up to 12,000 feet and
on Axel Heiberg Island up to 7,000 or 8,000 feet.   Both
topographically and geologically, therefore, the belt differs
fundamentally from the Canadian Shield and the Interior
Plains, its immediate neighbors.   Little is known as yet
about its mineral resources.

In the whole area of Canada north of 55°, the following are the main producers and expected producers. Their variety suggests what may very well occur elsewhere in this vast territory.

METALLICS

Gold

At the present time gold is being produced from two sources, the placer gravels of the Yukon and the lode deposits in the Yellowknife region north of Great Slave Lake. Lode deposits are primary ones, found in bed rock. Placer deposits are of a secondary nature, formed by the wearing away or destruction of lode deposits. For example, the gold of the Yukon gravels was originally in primary quartz veins in bed rock of the Yukon upland. Frost, rain, streams, etc. wore down the rock, and the gold, being heavy, was concentrated at the base of the resultant gravels that accumulated in valleys. In other words, Nature did the original mining of the primary deposits, performing much of the work than man now has to do in lode mining.

The story of gold in the Yukon is one of the most fascinating chapters in Canadian mining. In 1896 phenomenal finds of gold were made on Bonanza creek and during the next three or four years the gold-bearing area was extended to about 800 square miles, the richer gravels being located on streams tributary to the Klondike River, a branch of the Yukon. The rush that followed the discovery brought some 30,000 people to the area over routes that involved almost incredible hardships.

The focal point of the area was Dawson City, named after George M. Dawson, the intrepid director of the Geological Survey of Canada from 1895 until his death in 1901, who had done pioneer geological exploration in the Cordilleran Region and has been called the real discoverer of the Yukon Territory. Production of gold reached its peak in 1900 when a value of over twenty-two million dollars was recovered. By 1910 the richer gravels were worked out. Since then, however, a fairly steady production has been maintained by hydraulic mining and by dredging. Production from placer operations also comes from other areas in the Yukon such as Mayo, Whitehorse, Kluane Lake, and in northern Brtish Columbia from the Atlin area.

Besides these placer deposits, primary or lode deposits carrying gold also occur in northern British Columbia and the Yukon. These are related to the deep-seated igneous rocks, the largest mass of which is known as the Coast Range batholith. Important factors in the development of such properties, beside grade and tonnage, are access and transportation.

An important gold-bearing belt on the Shield extends from the north shore of Lake Athabasca northwest to an east and west line lying about halfway between Great Slave Lake and Great Bear Lake. With the development of aeroplane transportation following the war of 1914-18 and the discovery of rich radium and silver ores on Great Bear Lake there was great activity in prospecting this belt. Gold was found on the north shore of Lake Athabasca and in the Yellowknife area north of Great Slave Lake. The deposits discovered are of several types and are representative of what may be expected to occur elsewhere in the northern part of the Shield.

Discovery of gold on the north shore of Lake Athabasca took place in 1934 near what later became the town of Goldfields. An interesting feature in connection with the discoveries was that they occurred in granite and as a result a great deal more attention began to be paid by prospectors to areas underlain by that rock than had previously been the case. The two principal properties were the Box and the Athona. The former was taken over by the Consolidated Mining and Smelting Company and a 1,000-ton mill erected. A hydroelectric plant was built on Wellington River about 22 miles from Goldfields and a water supply for it secured by diverting the waters of Tazin Lake through a chain of smaller lakes to the site. When the mill commenced operations in 1939 some four million dollars had been expended including a million and a half on the power plant. In 1940 the milling rate was 1,400 tons a day. The grade of the ore was $1.676 per ton and the operating profit for the year was $59,000. Owing to a shortage of manpower, operations were suspended in May 1942. Since 1949, however, the company has supplied power to the properties of the Eldorado Mining and Refining Limited north of Beaverlodge Lake.

The Yellowknife gold producing area lies northeast of the north arm of Great Slave Lake in the basin of the Yellowknife River. Prospecting was active in the early thirties and production on several properties began in 1938. The deposits are of two main types; first, gold-bearing quartz veins occupying fractures and shear zones[3] in ancient volcanic and sedimentary rocks; and second, huge shear zones in places over 150 feet in width, trending north-northeast. In the latter type the ore consists of grey schist[4] with quartz amounting to from 30 to 75 percent. Some native gold occurs, but most of the precious value comes from two sulphides, arsenopyrite and pyrite. In 1951 gold to the amount of over 200,000 fine ounces was produced.

Copper-Nickel-Cobalt, etc.

An early interest in the mineral possibilities of the far north arose in connection with copper. In 1769 Governor Norton of Prince of Wales's Fort, the Hudson's Bay Company's great stone stronghold at the mouth of the Churchill

---

3. Breaks where the movement has been to and fro, grinding up the rock. Such zones are likely places for mineral material to be deposited.
4. Schists are platy rocks formed from earlier sedimentary or igneous rocks by heat and pressure.

River, sent Samuel Hearne to investigate the source of the
pieces of native copper which Indians were bringing to the
fort.   On his third attempt Hearne eventually reached the
Coppermine River but found no large deposits of the metal.
Later prospecting has had but little better results.   Native
copper occurs over a very great zone, but amounts large
enough and rich enough to be mined profitably have not as
yet been located.

Manitoba and Saskatchewan became important producers of copper-zinc-gold-silver when the important Flin
Flon ore-body, discovered in 1914 on the provincial boundary line, was brought into production by the Hudson Bay
Mining and Smelting Company. The purchase of the
property, the building of a smelter, and the development of
hydroelectric power at Island Falls on Churchill River, each
of which meant an expenditure of about five million dollars,
resulted in the opening up of one of the large mining operations of Canada.   The amount of ore mined annually is
over 1,500,000 tons, from which nearly 40,000 tons of blister
copper[5] are sent from the mill to the Montreal East refinery
of Canadian Copper Refiners Limited.

Though Flin Flon lies just south of fifty-five, two
other important sulphide properties lie north of that
parallel.   On one of these, mining operations have now
ceased and on the other they are just beginning.   The
former is the Sherritt-Gordon mine, 40 miles northeast of
Flin Flon.   From the time recoveries began in March 1931
to the closing down of the mill in September 1951 the
property produced 366,244,806 pounds of copper as well as
important quantities of zinc.   The Lynn Lake deposit of
Sherritt-Gordon Mines Limited lies about 120 miles almost
due north of Sherridon, the site of the Company's older
property.   The news of the discovery became known in the
autumn of 1945 and led to a great deal of prospecting in the

5. Smelted copper before being refined by electrolysis.

area. On the closing up of the mine at Sherridon the mining and milling equipment was transferred to the new camp for operations to begin in the fall of 1953. Over 14,000,000 tons of ore have been proved by drilling. It is planned to mine 2,000 tons a day. The annual output is expected to be 8,500 tons of nickel, 4,500 tons of copper, 150 tons of cobalt, and 70,000 tons of ammonium sulphate.

In British Columbia, copper showings occur over a wide area at the head of Portland Canal. In the Atlin district not far from the Yukon boundary gold-silver-copper-lead-zinc ores are being mined locally.

Lead-Zinc-Silver

The great lead-zinc-silver region of Canada is the southern part of British Columbia. But deposits have also been worked in the northern part of the province as at Hazelton and the Portland Canal region, and also in the Yukon, particularly the Mayo district.

An interesting region in which deposits of quite another type occur lies southwest of Pine Point on the south shore of the western part of Great Slave Lake. The region is flat and marked by sink-holes and the underlying rock is dolomite. The ore minerals are galena and sphalerite, sulphides of lead and zinc respectively, and the deposits bear a general similarity to the famous zinc-lead deposits of Missouri.

Uranium

The two main areas in Canada where radioactive minerals are known to occur both lie north of fifty-five. One is at the east end of Great Bear Lake in the Northwest Territories and the other is in the extreme northwest corner of the province of Saskatchewan, north of Lake Athabasca. The discovery in the former area was made in 1930 by two prospectors, Gilbert Labine and E. C. St. Paul. They had flown in to investigate an occurrence of cobalt which had been reported by J. MacKintosh Bell who, assisted by Charles Camsell, had investigated the area for the Geological Survey of Canada in 1900. The presence of cobalt suggested that silver might also be there. It was, and was accompanied also by something more valuable—pitchblende, a variety of the radioactive mineral, uraninite. The deposit was staked for the Eldorado Gold Mining Company and became known as the Eldorado Mine. Up to this time the chief source of radium had been the Belgian Congo where deposits had been brought into large scale production in 1924. The discovery of the Canadian deposit ended to a very considerable extent the Belgian monopoly. When during World War II progress was made in atomic fission it was necessary to find a large source of uranium. The Canadian Government, therefore, secured shares of the Eldorado Company and the project was transferred to a Crown Company, the Eldorado Mining and Refining (1944) Limited. Numerous other occurrences of uraninite have been located in the Northwest Territories, all of which are found in the rocks of the Shield. They occur particularly in two main belts, one extending from near the northeast corner of Great Bear Lake to near the north arm of the Great Slave Lake. The other is along the east arm of Great Slave Lake.

Most of the discoveries of the other important region, that of Lake Athabasca, are concentrated in an area with a radius of about 12 miles centered at Goldfields. Other discoveries lie farther east on the Fond du Lac and Stony Rapids-Porcupine River regions. The discovery of uranium in the Goldfields area was made in 1935 on the Nicholson property by the shore of the lake about two miles east of Goldfields. Since then several thousand occurrences have been located: drilling has been done on many properties and underground exploration has been carried out on some of the more important ones. A large production appears to be assured.

Iron

The highgrade iron deposits along the Labrador-Quebec boundary form one of the great mineral assets of Canada. The main occurrences so far developed are in the Knob Lake area just south of latitude 55°. Here some forty properties of high-grade ore have been located within a length of 90 miles and a maximum width of 14 miles. At the end of 1950 proven ore amounted to over four hundred million tons and it is expected that further search will show many times this tonnage. Ore shipments will begin this year.

The mineralized belt continues to the northwest and prospecting has revealed extensive iron deposits along the west side of Ungava Bay in amounts estimated in hundreds of millions of tons. The grade, however, is considerably lower than that of the Knob Lake ore and therefore concentration would be necessary. Shipment would be by water. The region affords a great potential reserve of iron for Canada and the world.

NON-METALLICS

Coal

Occurrences of coal are known at a number of places in the northern Rocky Mountains, the interior Cordillera, the Mackenzie River valley, and the arctic islands. At Carmacks in the Yukon and in the Groundhog area of northern British Columbia the deposits are of Lower Cretaceous (Kootenay) age. A little lignite of Tertiary age has been mined about forty miles north of Dawson.

Oil

A large petroleum field lies along the Mackenzie River in the eastern part of the Mackenzie Mountain area. The productive locality is Norman Wells where the annual production is over two hundred thousand barrels of crude oil.   This was the source of the oil for the wartime Canol Project, but now the output is being used for local needs. The oil is obtained from beds of Upper Devonian age.

Along the Athabasca River north of Waterways—the terminal of the Northern Alberta Railway running north from Edmonton—are outcroppings of bituminous sands which contain almost fabulous amounts of heavy petroleum material.   The thick overburden and the distance from markets have been factors in delaying the development of this great potential wealth.

Asbestos

When one speaks of asbestos in Canada the first thought is of the Eastern Townships of Quebec with its mines at Thetford, Black Lake, and Danville.   It is of interest to note that in the McDame Lake area of northern British Columbia is also a large deposit being developed by Cassiar Asbestos Corporation, Limited.

––––––––––

Much has been learned about northern Canada since the days when Samuel Hearne went to the Coppermine River to look for deposits of native copper.   For a long time travel and prospecting were limited to the main canoe routes. Even such work, however, revealed mineral showings, some of which, as has been pointed out, resulted in production. Today with an ever growing knowledge of the geology of this vast region and the revolution in travel, brought about by the use of the aeroplane, it can confidently be expected that many other valuable deposits will be discovered in addition to those known today.

*Staff-Sergeant H. Kearney has served with the R.C.M.P.
since 1927, in the Yukon, Alberta, New Brunswick, and the
Eastern Arctic. Since 1935, when he left the most northerly
Police detachment, on Ellesmere Island, he has been stationed at "G" Division H.Q. in Ottawa, where he is now in
charge of that division's criminal investigation branch.
From there he has made periodic trips into the Arctic, including one to the Belcher Islands in connection with the
celebrated Eskimo murders of 1941.*

Policing the North

by H. KEARNEY

THE Royal Canadian Mounted Police is the sole law
enforcement body in the Northwest Territories and
the Yukon, and its authority for the policing of both is
contained in the Royal Canadian Mounted Police Act,
which is a federal statute. Thus, the Force is responsible
for the enforcement of all laws, federal statutes, including
the Criminal Code, territorial ordinances and certain
municipal by-laws.

The constitutions of these territories are contained in
the Northwest and Yukon Territories Acts, both of which
are federal statutes. Authority for the administration of
government in the Northwest Territories devolves upon a
commissioner under instruction of the Governor in Council
or the minister of the Department of Northern Affairs and
National Resources. The commissioner is appointed by

the Governor in Council and has a council of eight, five of whom are appointed by the Governor in Council and three who are elected by the residents of the territories. The Commissioner of the R.C.M.P. is an appointed member. Sessions of the council are held in the Northwest Territories and in Ottawa.

A similar arrangement exists with regard to the Yukon, except that the commissioner for that territory has a council of five, all of whom are elected by residents of the Yukon. Council sessions are held in the Yukon.

The Northwest Territories and the Yukon each have two municipalities; Yellowknife and Hay River in the former, Whitehorse and Dawson in the latter, and each elects its own municipal council.

The 1951 census for the Northwest Territories showed a population of 16,004, consisting of 6,344 whites, 3,838 Indians and 6,822 Eskimos. For the same year the Yukon had a population of 10,096 consisting of 8,533 whites, 1,533 Indians and 30 Eskimos. The population of these territories fluctuates with the coming and going of seasonal workers employed in mining, prospecting for oil and minerals, on construction and transportation work. Travellers and some tourists go to and from the Yukon and Alaska on the Alaska Highway. Many other tourists travel to the Yukon via steamship from west coast ports to Skagway, Alaska, thence by rail to Whitehorse, Y.T.

"G" Division of the R.C.M.P. is charged with policing the Northwest Territories and the Yukon, the extreme northern parts of Alberta and British Columbia, the James Bay Districts of Ontario and Quebec and the northern part of Quebec. Headquarters of "G" Division, under command of Superintendent H. A. Larsen, of *St. Roch* fame, is at Ottawa, and is divided into four sub-divisions, with headquarters for the Yukon Territory situated at Whitehorse, for the southern part of the district of Mackenzie at Fort Smith, N.W.T.; for the northern part of the District of Mackenzie at Aklavik; and for the Eastern Arctic at division headquarters in Ottawa.

With the exception of the offence of being drunk and disorderly which is perhaps more prevalent in the district of Mackenzie and the Yukon than in other parts of Canada, crimes and offences are on a par with those elsewhere. The rather steady occupancy of the R.C.M.P. guardroom at Whitehorse is attributed largely to non-permanent residents with a frontier state of mind.

From the standpoint of policing, a great change began in 1942 when the building of the Alaska Highway, of pipe-lines and of new air-ports, as well as the enlarging of old air-ports, began. Thousands of workers poured into the territories, and in the Yukon the old mode of travel gave way to motor vehicles and aircraft. In the Northwest Territories the sled dog and boat held their own except in the more settled areas surrounding Fort Smith, Yellowknife, Hay River, and two or three detachments where travel by motor vehicle was possible. Today a police aircraft, based at Fort Smith, is available for patrol work and other duties throughout the Mackenzie district and the Western Arctic.

On the whole, the Indians of the territories are fairly law-abiding, but there are exceptions among those living close to the settlements. Many of these, gaining access to liquor through connections among the whites, fall into crime and indolence to the complete neglect of their families.

Common crimes and offences are almost non-existent amongst the Eskimos, and murder when it appears usually results from some primitive motive related to existence and self-preservation. But crimes of passion, such as murder for the possession of women, do occur. An insane person was often put to death for the protection of the band, and customary among the Eskimos was the request of an aged person to be done away with. Some time ago a woman shot her husband because he was a poor provider. Her second marriage resulted in protracted spells of loneliness for, if unsuccessful in the hunt, her new husband maintained a discreet distance.

The highest court in the Northwest Territories is that of a stipendiary magistrate who has jurisdiction equivalent to a Superior Court judge in the provinces, while in the Yukon there is a territorial court presided over by a judge.

All R.C.M.P. guardrooms in both the Northwest Territories and the Yukon are common gaols and penitentiaries. This means that a prisoner may serve a sentence of any length at an R.C.M.P. guardroom. However, in practice, prisoners sentenced to penitentiary terms, that is two years or over, are transferred to penitentiaries in the provinces and many of those receiving lesser sentences, particularly the unruly, are transferred to the Alberta provincial common gaol at Fort Saskatchewan. Officers commanding the R.C.M.P. at Whitehorse, Fort Smith and Aklavik have the authority of wardens and are thus empowered to impose discipline and punishment upon insubordinate prisoners. The average number of prisoners serving sentences in R.C.M.P. guardrooms at Fort Smith and Whitehorse at any one time is about fourteen, not counting overnight prisoners charged mostly with being drunk and disorderly and with vagrancy.

In addition to ordinary police work, that is the enforcement of law and order and the investigation of offences, the R.C.M.P. in the Northwest Territories and the Yukon have always performed a great deal of civil administrative work on behalf of the two governing bodies of the territories and for other departments of the Federal Government. This, to a large extent, has been occasioned by the fact that the R.C.M.P. were for a time the only representatives of the Government in the territories. At present, and despite the fact that for some years past other government employees have been stationed there and have relieved the police of certain duties, an increase in the volume of work finds the Force doing more administrative work than ever.

On behalf of the Department of Northern Affairs and National Resources, members of the Force act as game guardians and attend to the compiling of native game returns, the forwarding of general reports on game conditions, the issuing of game licences and enforcement of the game laws. In the Northwest Territories, the police act as registrars of vital statistics, notaries public and commissioners of oaths, issuers of family allowances and trading and trafficking licences, collectors of fur export and income tax, game licence and business licence fees. Similar duties are performed in the Yukon. At Old Crow a member holds the appointment of immigration inspector.

The Force ministers to the welfare of the Eskimos in the issuing of relief rations, the payment of family allowances in kind and other services.

Under the Department of Indian Affairs, members administer relief to destitute Indians, accompany Indian agents on treaty payment trips and supervise payment of family allowances at Fort Smith, N.W.T., Fort Chimo, P.Q., and other places. At Whitehorse, a member of the Force acts as veterinary inspector for the Department of Agriculture. For the Department of Fisheries members of the police are fisheries officers for the enforcement of the Fisheries Act and Regulations and they also issue the various classes of fishery licences.

At Old Crow and Aklavik, the police act as collectors of customs. At Fort Smith and Aklavik, the officers commanding are district inspectors of income tax.

Members in charge of detachments at Chesterfield Inlet, Lake Harbour, Frobisher Bay, Alexandra Fiord, Pangnirtung, Pond Inlet, Craig Harbour, Baker Lake, and Eskimo Point, all in the Eastern Arctic, and at Port Harrison, P.Q., hold appointments as postmasters.

Under the Department of Citizenship and Immigration, a member is appointed judge of the court at Fort Smith and another member judge of the court for the Eastern Arctic for hearing applications for citizenship. The police also act as inspectors of weights and measures for the Department of Trade and Commerce and enforce regulations respecting aircraft and shipping under the Department of Transport. On behalf of the Quebec provincial government, members of the Force act as registrars of vital statistics for Indians and Eskimos and as special game wardens in northern Quebec.

The R.C.M.P. have had detachments in the Western Arctic and at Chesterfield Inlet on the west coast of Hudson Bay for about forty-six years. Herschel Island detachment in the Western Arctic was established as early as 1904 and Cape Fullerton detachment, near Chesterfield Inlet, was first established in 1903. In 1921, the Force began establishing detachments in the Eastern Arctic, first on Baffin Island then on Devon and Ellesmere Islands. The part played by the R.C.M.P. detachments in maintaining sovereignty of the Arctic islands is of the utmost importance, and no less were the voyages of the R.C.M.P. schooner, *St. Roch*, through the Northwest Passage.

Many outstanding patrols were made by members stationed at the former Dundas Harbour and Bache Peninsula detachments and at Craig Harbour detachment. These were to a large extent exploratory and contributed much to a knowledge of the north. Members collected specimens of sea mammals, flora and fauna and items of geological

A member of the R.C.M.P. (left) and a fur trader help three Eskimos with a fish net on the shore of the Arctic Ocean.   R. N. Hourde

At Fort Good Hope on the Mackenzie, a Mounted Police constable takes the temperature of a Hare Indian baby.   Geo. Hunter

A police boat at the Mackenzie's mouth.   R. N. Hourde

In the sunshine of early spring, a policeman calls on an old trapper who lives alone in his log shack.
                                                          Ralph Cash

Sgt. (now Supt.) Larsen, on patrol from the icebound "St. Roch" in the central Arctic, harnesses his dog-team in the "Nome hitch." L. A. Learmonth

Dogs in the tandem hitch of the woodland trails haul a canvas sided toboggan. Harrington for HBC

Packsack, bedroll, and grub-box make a well balanced load on a portage. Harrington for HBC

Two Indians take a canoe down some rapids. The square stern is for the outboard motor.
N. Morant for HBC

Small power vessels like this triple-screw diesel tug of the HBC have replaced the picturesque sternwheelers on the Mackenzie.   L. A. Learmonth

Eskimo boats cluster round an Eastern Arctic supply ship.   J. W. Anderson

A glider at Coppermine, released by a Dakota on Exercise Muskox, disgorges its freight onto a sled pulled by a Penguin.   Canadian Army

Bucking deep drifts, a double-header tractor-swing crosses a frozen lake along a "trail" marked by small trees.   R. Harrington

A Canso amphibian brings supplies to Arctic Bay, northern Baffin Island.
J. Cormack

At Yellowknife the gaping mouth of a Bristol Freighter opens to receive heavy equipment for a remote mining camp.
Geo. Hunter

A vital link in r
thern defence is
Royal Canad
Corps of Sign
These two memb
man the N.W.T.
Yukon Radio Sys
station at Fort W
ley on the Mack
zie River.

Geo. Hu

On Exercise Muskox, one Penguin tows another out of a hole into which
it has dropped.   Canadian Army

interest, many of which were sent to the National Museum of Canada. In addition they took weather readings which were transmitted to the Dominion meteorological office via the annual supply ship.

Life was severe and precarious at these early outposts and when, on occasion, the supply ship failed to reach its destination due to ice conditions, detachment men were cut off from civilization for as long as three years. When the ship did succeed in making its way through, it rarely stayed more than a few hours and if shortly after its departure a serious illness or fatality occurred, the outside world knew nothing of it until the following year. Under such conditions and for their contributions to an understanding of the North, much credit is due the men who manned these outposts in the days prior to polar aviation and radio contact with civilization.

*Philip H. Godsell, F.R.G.S., served the Hudson's Bay
Company twenty years, starting as an apprentice clerk in
1906 and rising to the position of inspecting officer in the
Northwest. In the course of his duties he travelled thousands of miles in the North, on snowshoes, on horseback, and
by canoe, York boat, and dog sled.*

Old Time Travel

by PHILIP H. GODSELL

THE coming of the aeroplane to the far north shortly after
the first Great War began a revolution in northern
travel. Journeys which had for centuries taken weeks by
canoe and dog-team were now accomplished in a matter of
hours. But though the aeroplane has improved vastly in
range and dependability since those first hazardous flights,
it still has its limitations. During the summer, in all the
vast area of the Canadian Northland, Indian and white
trapper, prospector and traveller, still depend on the canoe
for "inside" trips, from the break-up in May till freeze-up
in October; and hardly a consignment of freight goes into
the North without its accompanying load of factory-made
canoes. Fully forty-percent of the more northerly areas
consists of lakes and streams where, aside from air travel, the
canoe is still the only practical method of summer transportation.

In winter, too, the northern traveller depends on the traditional forms of travel for short trips and even, in the Arctic, for long ones.

Anyone wishing to recapture some of the romance and colour of the early days of exploration can still do so if he cares to plan a canoe trip through the unspoiled wilderness. Apart from fishing there are daily thrills in the "jumping" of white water as one traverses foaming stretches of turbulent rivers bounding towards Hudson Bay or the Polar Sea; the sight of feeding moose and deer in the small grassy lakes and the broods of recently-hatched wildfowl, or to find one's moccasined feet traversing portage trails that were old before the first white man set foot upon the continent.

In making such a trip the standard, canvas-covered, factory-made canoes have long superseded the birch-bark, the various models being admirably adapted to whatever type of work happens to be required. The canoe should be close-ribbed for strength, and weigh from 65 to 75 pounds so that it can be easily carried on the shoulders of one man by tying the paddles lengthway to the thwarts in such a way that they will rest upon the shoulders when making a portage. It should have a beam of from 32″ to 35″, and a depth of at least 12½″, and the load should be carefully balanced before starting out so that the bow rises with the waves. The best paddles are those made by Indians from birch, cut to a point at the end of the blade so that they can be used when poling in rapids or up-stream. An additional paddle should always be carried, along with a length of extra heavy canvas, white lead, tin and tacks for repairs in case a hole is punched in the bottom from rocks or underwater snags. A tent, a tarpaulin, a leather portage-strap, a bedroll, grub-box, axe, file, tea-pail and frying pan about rounds out the necessary equipment for a prolonged cruise, while, in the event of a fair wind, a blanket can always be hoisted on a make-shift mast, trimmed from a small spruce, as an extemporaneous sail.

Today, almost every canoe that threads these northern waterways is equipped with a gasoline engine, while brigades of Indian canoes are often to be encountered, strung one behind the other, towed by an Indian in the lead canoe with its stuttering outboard. So accustomed, in fact, have the red men become to this aid to daily labour that, when I sent for an Indian at Fort Resolution to take a prospector over to Pine Point, a short eighteen miles away, in his canoe, he pronounced the trip impossible—*his outboard motor had broken down!*

From freeze-up, late in October, until April, when the snow becomes soft and the ice treacherous, the dog-team used to reign supreme throughout the North until the coming of the aeroplane. Perhaps the two great centres where this means of transportation had reached its highest development and efficiency were Norway House at the head of Lake Winnipeg and Fort Chipewyan on Lake Athabasca, the former the Hudson's Bay Company's headquarters for the District of Keewatin and the latter for the once far-flung Athabasca District. In these two regions "tripping" to the Indian camps in winter became a recognized form of competition between the Company's men and the so-called "free traders." Spies kept watch on each other's trading posts, and word of a big fur catch at some distant Indian camp, brought in by "moccasin telegraph," would be the signal for the traders to hastily throw together trading outfits, and lash them on toboggans along with the requisite supply of dog-feed and rations, and for the trippers to set out on a wilderness marathon with their dog-teams, each vying with the other to reach the camp first and display his wares. For to the first-comer usually went the bulk, and cream, of the spoils, the Indians entering into the spirit of the game by reserving for the losing team only a few of their poorest skins. This spirit of competition and rivalry developed a demand for the fastest and most durable Indian or half-breed runners as trippers, as well as the hardiest and fastest sleigh-dogs, and the stories of their prowess are still sagas of Northern hearths and campfires.

One of the first lessons learned upon the trail was to take the greatest care of the feet, always changing socks and moccasins night and morning and to avoid, at all costs, wearing moccasins that were over-tight and would cripple one eventually. This is a lesson that applies as much to the modern dog-driver and snowshoe traveller as it did in days gone by, and will greatly ease and facilitate foot travel.

Travelling in deep snow in mid-winter a day's journey usually constitutes an average of twenty-five miles which, under such conditions, is considered "good going," though, in the spring, when the snow melts on top and forms a frozen crust strong enough to support a man without snow-shoes, "long days" can be made with comparatively little effort, giving the driver a chance to ride over frozen lakes and rivers on his toboggan. Under such conditions almost unbelievable distances are covered between sunrise and dark. In the spring of 1906 the late William Ogston made a trip from his post at Trout Lake House to Norway House, covering the five hundred miles in five days—and making an equally spectacular return trip to his post.

The old Hudson's Bay ration to "trippers" was two frozen whitefish per dog per night; 2 pounds of flour, three-quarters of a pound of "sowbelly," or bacon, two ounces of tea, two ounces of sugar, and one plug of niggerhead tobacco per tripper per day. This was usually supplemented by fish or meat obtained at Indian cabins and wigwams en route, and the number of days' rations depended upon the distance between posts on the basis of twenty-five miles a day. Modern dog-team travellers usually contrive to cook up their pork-and-beans, bannock, and small, ground meat patties ahead of time, permit them to freeze then dump them, frozen, into grub-sacks, to be lashed at the rear of the toboggan along with the inevitable grub-box containing an enamelware cup, plate, knife, fork, spoon, etc., together with cotton bags containing tea and sugar, matches and what other culinary requisites they happen to fancy, always keeping the weight to a minimum. Around the campfire the bannocks are thawed before the blaze while chunks of frozen pork-and-beans are tossed with a scoopful of snow into a frying pan and a hot meal is ready within a very short space of time, with steaming tea to round it off and help fortify the traveller for the further miles of snow-shoeing ahead. Tea, it might be mentioned, has a revitalizing and energizing quality that all other drinks lack, and continues to hold its place as the beverage *par excellence* upon the trail.

While, today, the aeroplane has replaced the dog-team for long journeys, and the organized commercial "tripping" to Indian camps has largely become a thing of the past, the dog-team still endures and the *parki*-clad trapper, trader and traveller is still to be seen wending the narrow trails through snow-mushroomed pines, and camping in the wilderness under exactly the same conditions as those of old.

Here and there the basket-sleigh of the Yukon and Alaska, with its handles protruding in the rear, has super-seded the standard toboggan, while in places where open country permits, dogs are harnessed two by two with a spike dog in the lead; but, generally speaking, the old sixteen-inch-wide toboggan, either of birch or oak, con-tinues to remain the favourite.

Experienced Indian guides can still be secured from the factor of any northern Hudson's Bay Company post, and this is always preferable to picking one haphazardly from an Indian camp, while the same applies to Eskimo guides and snowhouse builders when contemplating a winter journey in the Arctic. From long experience I have always preferred Cree guides and dog-drivers to those of any other tribe since they are more agile, resourceful and untiring, and are not so apt to become morose and awkward as are those of Athapascan blood such as the Chipewyans and Slavies, while the Ojibways are inclined to be slow and plodding. And, no Indian can make a comfortable night camp in the winter woods with greater despatch and efficiency than the Cree. Today, of course, the small portable tent and collapsible stove, carried in a crate on the tail of the toboggan, has largely obviated the outside winter camp, and gives a greater measure of comfort to the traveller.

Along the arctic coast the ice-shod *kahmotik*, capable of carrying a load of from eight hundred pounds to a ton, with its fan-shaped team of hauling dogs, each attached to a separate trace by a harness, continues to form a major link in travel and transportation. Sled-runners are first mudded then planed to a bevelled edge in the centre, after which water is squirted from the mouth to freeze into a wide, glassy surface which, when properly levelled off, gives a minimum resistance to frozen snow crystals once the heavily-loaded sled is on the move.

Working the *kahmotik* over up-ended pressure-ridges of ice, however, furnishes its own difficulties in this form of transport, especially when the carefully prepared ice-runners become chipped, necessitating a repair job in the bitter cold. Also, the comparative comfort of an outside camp in the deep pine forests with a roaring fire to at least thaw that part of the traveller closest to the blaze is lacking. Instead, its place is taken by the hastily-erected snow igloo—which can be thrown up in around forty-five minutes by an experienced Eskimo guide and is constructed from snow-blocks cut from drifted snow that must of necessity be in one stratum only. Raised at an elevation of two feet across half the circumference of the igloo is the snow-bed upon which fur sleeping bags are laid upon an insulation of caribou skins or netted willows. On another snow-block reposes the hissing Primus-stove which, despite its small size, has long since been considered an essential in Polar travel, whereon a hot meal can be prepared in short order while the dogs are devouring their ration of frozen seal-meat or tom-cod without. For lighter, and faster, travel the basket-sled mounted on runners is sometimes used in preference to the heavier *kahmotik*, in which case the traveller suits his own fancy as to the kind of hitch he uses, whether the single hitch, or the fan-shaped type more favoured in the Eastern Arctic.

Until white traders and explorers adopted the Eskimo mode of dress and the Eskimo snowhouse when travelling, Arctic expeditions were frequently beset with tragic failure. While Vilhjalmur Stefansson was the first advocate of the application of Eskimo methods to Polar travel as an effective means of combating the exigencies of life in the "friendly" Arctic—which, it must be admitted, does not display these friendly attributes too often—Mounted Police and old-time whalers had already realized the advantages to be derived by studying the ways of these intelligent and adaptable natives.

Mounted Police and traders along the arctic coast have long since discovered that heavy woollen clothing of white manufacture is totally unsuited to life in this region. Instead, the everyday garb of the Eskimos—which is negligible in weight, windproof and warm, and can, with proper care, be kept dry and serviceable for days on end from the body heat alone—has become the standard wear for Polar travel.

This consists of a hooded inner shirt, trousers and long socks of fawn-skin, the silky hair being worn next to the body, while the outer garments comprise another hooded shirt and trousers of long-haired caribou-skins, and boots, frequently made from the legs of these animals, worn over the socks. Polar-bearskin, or caribou-skin, mittens, suspended from the neck by a cord, complete the outfit.

Care is taken to avoid over-heating the body, since excessive perspiration will not be absorbed by the under-garments, resulting in the lowering of the body temperature to a dangerous degree and causing frost to form between the layers of clothing. Upon entering an igloo the seasoned wayfarer will pull the outer shirt over his head and carefully whip all signs of frost and snow from the fur with a light willow stick so that the warmer temperature will not cause it to melt and soak into the deer skin. The same care is taken with trousers, boots and sleeping-bags.

Where the Eskimo is concerned both he and his wife invariably discard all clothing before crawling into the fur bag at night. By observing these precautions one can continue to travel day after day in the same clothing without it becoming hardened with frost, or unfit for use.

Today many of the old time forms of northern transportation are no more. The strident racket of outboard motors and the stuttering cough of the diesels are heard in the land, while overhead the humming aeroplane wings its way to the farthest outposts of the North, carrying the luxuries of civilization to the doors of our modern pioneers. But in their smaller sphere, canoe, *kahmotik*, dog-toboggan and snowshoes continue, as they have done for countless generations in the past, to do their part in transportation and travel, and in pushing back the frontier from the prairies to the polar sea.

Colonel Andrew Croft, D.S.O., M.A., F.R.G.S., of the Essex Regt., was second in command of the Oxford University Arctic Expedition in 1935-6, and during the late war served largely in Scandinavia. After the war he was assistant director of scientific research for the War Office, specialising in arctic and mountain warfare, and represented the War Office on Exercise Musk-Ox. He has contributed many articles on arctic travel and transport to scientific magazines, and is the author of Polar Exploration *and joint author of* Under the Pole Star. *At present he is serving with the chief of army field forces at Fort Monroe, Virginia.*

Transport Today

by ANDREW CROFT

Mobility, as an old cavalryman once observed, is "to git thar fustest with the mostest." It is of course the key factor to progress and exploration in the Canadian Arctic. Only by improvements in transportation and by cutting down the costs can it become economical to make use of the vast resources of these regions.

The history of modern transport in the North dates back to the winter of 1920-21, when Imperial Oil Limited introduced the airplane into arctic Canada. Until then, water transport offered the only fairly easy access into these regions, but was itself limited to a few months each summer. This entailed ocean transport from the Pacific to the Beaufort Sea, or from an Atlantic port to areas in the Eastern

Arctic, or more usually river transport on the Yukon and the mighty Mackenzie, which has often been called the main artery of northern Canada. Even to penetrate inland from the Mackenzie River meant weeks of preparation and perhaps months of toil on foot, by dog sled or by canoe.

The use of the airplane has changed the whole picture and made possible the rapid developments of the past two or three decades. The search for raw materials, combined with defence requirements during or since the Second World War, are largely responsible for the improvements in transportation which are now taking place.

First of all, let us examine the network of inland water-ways and the progress in construction of ocean-going ships for northern use; let us then consider the airfields and the types and potentialities of aircraft for freighting, rescue and amphibious operations; finally let us assess the availability of railways and roads and the employment and types of tractor trains and snowmobiles. At the same time we can study the collective use of these developments in an attempt to probe the future.

Water

Ever since the Northwest was first opened to commerce, water transport on the Yukon and Mackenzie River systems has borne the heaviest share of traffic. The Mackenzie and its tributaries, the Athabasca and Slave Rivers, provide a direct route by water of about 1,700 miles; subsidiary routes on Lake Athabasca, Great Slave Lake and Great Bear Lake increase this water system by more than 800 miles. Flowing from the west into the Slave and the Mackenzie, both the Peace and Liard Rivers have served as highways for exploration and water transport ever since the early pioneering days. At the southern end of this river and lake network, and only 300 miles north of Edmonton, is the

railway terminus of Waterways in Alberta.   From here,
freight is carried by water to Fort Fitzgerald, where the
16-mile portage to Fort Smith, over well maintained roads,
is necessary in order to avoid a series of rapids on the Slave
River.   From Fort Smith there is uninterrupted navigation
to the Arctic Ocean.

On this Mackenzie River system, general freight services
are maintained by three companies: The Northern Transportation Company, The Yellowknife Transportation Company, and The McInnis Products Corporation.   The
Hudson's Bay Company, which operated these services for
over 60 years, decided in 1947 to restrict its activities to the
supply of its own trading posts.   This company, however,
continues to supply the Western Arctic, through Tuktoy-
aktuk on the Arctic Ocean, from supply points on the
Mackenzie River.   These services extend as far east along
the coast as Spence Bay.   Many of the boats burn oil and
are equipped with two-way radio, which enables them to
keep in regular communication with stations en route.
Schooners operated by traders, Roman Catholic Missions or
Eskimos also provide occasional transport.   The carrying of
freight in ocean-going vessels from ports on the Pacific coast
is no longer considered economical.

In eastern Canada, the annual Eastern Arctic Patrol
was, until recently, operated by ships of the Hudson's Bay
Company.   However, in the summer of 1950, the C. D.
Howe, specially built for the purpose by the Canadian
Government, successfully carried out her maiden voyage.
This 2,600-ton vessel has a cruising radius of 10,000 miles,
will carry 88 passengers and 1,000 tons of cargo and is
equipped to patrol as far as Baffin Island and the more inaccessible central and northern arctic islands.   This involves
a voyage of more than 12,000 miles.   The helicopter carried
on board is used for ice reconnaissance, for air photography

and for transporting government officials. The ice-
breaker *N. B. McLean*, also operated by the Department
of Transport, assists vessels in the navigation of the Hudson
Bay route. Early in the season she enters Hudson Strait
for the inspection, repair and servicing of all navigational
aids, including buoys, lights and radio and direction-finding
stations. She also patrols the route and provides ships with
information about ice and weather conditions.

The Hudson's Bay Company has two ships operating
in the area of Hudson Bay: the *Rupertsland*, commissioned
in 1949, which serves the northern sector of the Bay,
southern Baffin Island and Hudson Strait, and the *Fort
Garry*, which serves the remainder of the Bay. Small
schooners operating out of Churchill also serve the coasts of
Hudson Bay. Power boats known as "Peterheads" provide
local transportation and may be found at nearly all the
Eastern Arctic settlements.

North of Lancaster Sound, there are now five arctic
weather stations, operated jointly by Canada and the
United States. Each summer a United States naval task
force provides the stations with supplies and relief personnel. The chief station, Resolute Bay on Cornwallis
Island, has a good airfield which is operational throughout
the year; it is also the most accessible by sea. The annual
naval task force to Resolute Bay usually consists of four
ships: two ice-breakers, a cargo ship and a tanker; only the
ice-breakers can reach Eureka and Alert. Long range
reconnaissance is carried out by R.C.A.F. Lancaster aircraft, and short range reconnaissance by light helicopter
from the ice-breakers. This cooperation between powerful
ice-breakers, reconnaissance by air and weather-forecasting
from shore is vital for success in such an enterprise.

New ships are becoming available for this northern
work. The C. G. S. *D'Iberville*, specifically built for

supplying the joint weather stations and visiting posts in
Baffin Island or further north, carried out a maiden voyage
to these areas during the summer of 1953.   A vessel of
3,055 tons, she is equipped to carry two Bell helicopters, 50
passengers and 350 tons of freight.   This year the new ice-
breaker for the Royal Canadian Navy, H.M.C.S. *Labrador*,
is due to be commissioned; she has a displacement of 5,400
tons and is a modification of the United States Coast Guard
Eastwind class.   Meanwhile, the United States Navy has
recently awarded a contract for the construction of the first
new ice-breaker it has had built since the end of the Second
World War.   She will be 310 feet long, with a beam of 76
feet and displacement of 8,300 tons.

Landing ships for tanks, or L.S.T.'s as they are generally
known, have been used both in Alaska and in the Eastern
Arctic for beach landings.   In Alaska, they have proved
to be invaluable for carrying bulk diesel fuel from an ocean-
going tanker to the piping and storage systems ashore. They
are also excellent for carrying cargo, but their thin skins
make them very vulnerable to ice damage; their chief asset
is the bow opening, which enables cargo to be delivered on
to the beach.   Marine laws of today, however, do not
permit these ships to handle commercial cargo unless the
bow doors are sealed, thus eliminating the L.S.T.'s greatest
advantage.

Air

Progress in the development and construction of airfields
was particularly rapid during the Second World War.
Airfields in the Northwest which can operate throughout
the year are situated at Fort Smith, Fort Resolution, Hay
River, Yellowknife, Fort Simpson and Norman Wells.   The
ones constructed at Fort Providence and Wrigley are now
used only during the summer months.   Passenger, freight

and express services by air are maintained throughout the year to many points in Mackenzie District. Canadian Pacific Air Lines maintain services daily, except Sundays, from Edmonton to Fort Smith and Yellowknife, via Mc-Murray. Weekly services are also provided to Hay River, via Peace River. Yellowknife in its turn runs services every two weeks to Rae, Indian Lake, Port Radium and Coppermine. Fort Providence, Fort Simpson, Norman Wells, Fort Good Hope, Arctic Red River, Fort Mc-Pherson and Aklavik have weekly services; Wrigley and Fort Norman are serviced by Norman Wells. Some of these flights have to be suspended during the "break-up" and "freeze-up."

In the Eastern Arctic, commercial air services operate northward from Churchill in Manitoba and from Moosonee in Ontario, chiefly on a charter basis. During the war, landing fields were constructed on Southampton Island and at Frobisher Bay on Baffin Island to link up with bases in southern Greenland and at Churchill and Fort Chimo, P.Q. These landing fields, as well as the one at Baker Lake, are available for use when required.

The Second World War created the first real advance in air supply; in Burma, for instance, during a three-month period of severe fighting, the British 14th Army received 96 percent of its supplies by air. The Berlin air-lift was a dramatic example of what can be achieved in peacetime, while, during the Chinese offensive in Korea, air supply time after time saved the 8th Army from annihilation or surrender.

The C-47 Dakota, which has long been in the forefront of these operations, can still fly in rougher weather than any other two-engined plane now in large-scale use. With a 4,000-pound payload and ability to operate from a 2,500-foot air-strip, it makes an excellent bush plane, especially when equipped with ski for winter conditions.   The bush pilot's work-horse, however, is still the versatile, single-engined Norseman with a load capacity of 900 to 1,200 pounds and a five-hour gas supply; this payload is slightly reduced when skis are substituted for wheels and, increasingly so, when floats are fitted.   Though its sturdiness is still incomparable, the Norseman has immediate competitors in the De Havilland Beaver and Otter.   The first batch of six Canadian-built Otters was available in the spring of 1953.   The Otter's general robustness cannot yet be assessed, but its performance is considered to be an appreciable advance on both the Norseman and the Beaver.

Several aircraft developed during the recent war are still in general use in the North.   Of these, mention should perhaps be made of the Catalina or Canso flying boat, the U.S.A.F. Grumman Albatross flying boat and the U.S.A.F. B29 bomber, which has been converted for air sea-rescue and called the SB 29.   Due to the vast areas of water in the North, particularly during the summer months, flying boats perform a vital role as they are hardier than sea-planes. The primary mission of the SB 29 four-engined aircraft is to determine the position and effect the rescue of personnel stranded on water.   An A-3 airborne lifeboat is fitted by the gunwales to the bottom of the fuselage and over the outside of the bomb-bay.   It is deployed to the rescue area by parachute and guided to the survivors by remote control. The aircraft has a range of over 4,000 miles.

The best freighting plane yet used in arctic operation is the new U.S.A.F. three-decked, Douglas C-124, with a carrying capacity of 50,000 pounds.   It can lift the heaviest type of tractor and has the ability to operate from air strips less than a mile long.

The first models of the Chase, C-123, a U.S.A.F. medium assault transport, are now available, and it is expected that this aircraft will prove as satisfactory for use in the Arctic as in temperate climates. It can land on rough dirt fields, and, when jet-assisted, will take off from equally short fields fully loaded. On landing, the floor drops down at the rear to form a gently sloping ramp; heavy vehicles, up to a pay-load of 16,000 pounds, can then drive in and out of the aircraft under their own power. On a 300-mile lift, a C-123 can haul as much cargo as twenty 2½-ton trucks. At today's prices the cost of this assault transport is only about one third more than the cost of a fleet of twenty trucks. Admittedly fuel consumption is greater, but air supply requires fewer men to handle cargo.

The helicopter is still a primitive flying machine, but its contribution to arctic transportation is full of promise. It is not too far fetched to predict that within the next ten years the light types will compete favourably with the 2½-ton truck as the standard supply vehicle. Sikorski and Piasecki, who manufacture the largest helicopters, are now working on faster models which have a greater range and over-all performance. Jet-assisted and jet-driven heli-copters are also under consideration and the much advertised "convertiplane" is a virtual certainty for eventual produc-tion. This craft will take off and land vertically, and once in the air will fly like a fixed-wing plane.

Land

In regard to land transport in the North, railways are available from Skagway, near the Pacific coast, to White-horse on the Alaska Highway; from Edmonton to Dawson Creek, in eastern British Columbia, and to Peace River and to Waterways, in Alberta; and from Winnipeg, via The Pas, to Churchill on Hudson Bay.

Roads are also gradually being constructed to link up the more vital areas and, in particular, the mining centres.

The Alaska Highway was given a high priority and built at great speed during the Second World War, in order to connect Fairbanks in Alaska with the road from Edmonton to Dawson Creek, British Columbia. From the neighbourhood of Whitehorse on the Alaska Highway there is now a road leading northwards to Dawson on the Yukon River, and continuing west into Alaska, which takes much of the freight previously sent by river.

As a joint project between the Federal and Alberta Governments, an all weather road, the Mackenzie Highway, has been built from the railhead at Grimshaw in Alberta to Hay River on the south shore of Great Slave Lake; this provides an alternative route for the large mining community at Yellowknife. For about four months in summer time the journey across Great Slave is made by boat, whereas for approximately the same length of time during the winter a route is ploughed over the lake ice.

Although progress in aviation is pre-eminent, recent developments in overland transportation are significant. They can best be considered under three categories: *Landing Vehicles*, *Tractor Trains* and *Snowmobiles*.

The L.V.T. is a tracked, amphibious, landing vehicle which gave valuable service on seaborne, offensive operations in the later stages of the Second World War and again in Korea. It has also performed successfully in the re-supply of oil drilling operations in Alaska, when aircraft have been grounded and excessive thaw has precluded the use of any other type of overland transport.

The L.V.T. has the ability to swim across major rivers, and has hitherto proved to be the only vehicle for hauling 6,000-pound loads across arctic terrain at any time of the year. Unfortunately, due to its lightweight construction and highly stressed parts, maintenance has proved too costly on a ton-mile basis in comparison with tractors, and its use as a freighter has therefore been limited to emergency needs. Modifications are now being made to this vehicle, which may make it more practical for specialized work.

By far the most economical motive power for transporting freight is the heavy earth-moving tractor. Its use, however, is restricted to seasons when ground and ice are frozen firmly enough to support its heavy weight. When the summer thaw penetrates to a depth of more than two feet, its further employment becomes uneconomical.

There are various types of tractors; the heavier models are more dependable and efficient for large-scale operations and movement of heavy loads, whereas medium-weight tractors are less liable to break through the ice. The use of standard, or improvised, winter tracks increases the towing capacity by about 50 percent. Each tractor is provided with standard winter equipment, winches, belly hooks, radiator guards and covers. The lead tractor should be fitted with a V-type snow plough; other units may have angle-dozer blades, straight blades or no grading attachments. A dozer blade is normally a great asset since in addition to the primary purpose of moving snow or earth, it is used to break trail, protect the radiator and engine when travelling through timber, and to provide the necessary forward weight when negotiating a sudden rise or pitch.

The difficulties of winter travel make it highly advisable for at least three tractors to operate together as a unit. A "swing" normally consists of four to six tractors, each tractor towing three or four loaded bob-sleds. The load on each bob-sled varies according to the terrain, but usually weighs from 10,000 to 20,000 pounds.

In addition to the loaded bob-sleds, a large "swing" may haul two caravan-like huts, or "cabooses," mounted on bob-sleds; a normal sized swing, however, has only the one caboose which serves the dual role of messing and sleeping.

On lakes the trains usually travel several hundred yards apart for safety; on land they often stay close together in order to facilitate the doubling-up of tractors on hauls where one prime-mover is unable to pull its entire train. Cracks in the lake ice may become major obstacles to travel. In one case the ice parts in a wide crack; in the other it splits, and pressure pushes it up above the surface of the lake, sometimes higher than a man. If a low path cannot be found to cross this pressure ridge, a route is chiselled through it by dozer blades.

For long journeys it has been found impracticable to use drivers on shifts with continuous travelling. Crews do not get adequate rest in cabooses, pitching to and fro over typical arctic terrain; and a man's endurance under such conditions is about one week.

During the Second World War preparations were made for the possibility of fighting a winter campaign in Norway. Troops were trained for cold-weather warfare, and both Canada and the United States developed snowmobiles called respectively the Penguin and the Weasel. These, together with other equipment, were tried out towards the end of the war on the Canadian Exercises "Polar Bear," "Eskimo," and "Lemming," and after the war on "Musk-Ox." The Weasel is lighter and considerably less rugged than the Penguin, the laden weight of which is nearly five tons. Normally the Weasel's chief handicap is the so-called "one-ton, cargo sled" which it is designed to pull. This is too short for its width and altogether too rigid.

A most promising development by the Canadian Army, for eventual use with snowmobiles, is a bob-sled weighing 1,350 pounds which can take a payload of 4,000 pounds. In its design, emphasis has been placed on the utmost flexibility; with its articulating drawbar and spring suspension, the sled gives an unusually smooth ride and keeps the loading platform level over all but the most severe obstacles.

The snowmobile normally used on tractor train operations is the Canadian Bombardier. This is essentially a winter vehicle, as the front suspension is fitted with a pair of skis, five-feet long by one-foot wide, and only the rear suspension is tracked. The skis are naturally a disadvantage in heavily wooded country but on good surfaces the Bombardier can cruise at 25 to 30 miles per hour and carry 15 passengers or 2,500 pounds of freight.

As a result of military exercises, improvements are gradually being made in the design of snowmobiles; the Canadian Army has prototypes, in two weight classes, now undergoing trials. These are fully tracked vehicles with a ground pressure of less than two pounds per square inch, which enables them to have a good cross-country performance over snow or soft terrain. Meanwhile the United States Army Amphibious Cargo Carrier, M76, commonly called the Otter, has recently been accepted for production. It is fully tracked with a ground pressure comparable to that of the Canadian Army snowmobiles, and has other excellent characteristics, which should make it a most practicable vehicle for use throughout the year.

The reader may find this chapter too closely packed with detail to make easy reading, but the subject is as exciting in its potentialities as it is broad in scope. It is, however, wise to remember that the Far North is still an area for explorers, scientists and adventurers, even though its frontiers are gradually receding northward. Suitable transport is being developed for use on land, water and in the air, but many years will elapse before it becomes available in adequate quantity and the cost is often too high for small-scale enterprises. Progress still depends on man's will to do and learn; and the Arctic will continue to test his mettle.

After two and a half years of exploring in the Eastern Arctic, Graham W. Rowley joined the Canadian Army in 1939 and spent the next six years overseas. After the war he commanded the Baker Lake force of Exercise Musk-ox, and retired from the army as Lieut.-Col. to join the Defence Research Board where he was responsible for arctic research. He is now secretary and co-ordinator of the advisory committee on northern development in the Department of Northern Affairs and National Resources.

Defence of the Realm

by GRAHAM W. ROWLEY*

THE role of the Arctic in the defence of North America has never aroused any serious interest until quite recently. When in 1880 the United Kingdom passed to Canada all her rights in the Canadian Arctic there was very little response, and the purchase of Alaska from Russia by Seward in 1867 aroused more criticism in the United States than praise. It was known as "Seward's Ice-box" and "Seward's Folly" and even today Seward is justified far more often on the value of the gold and salmon exploited than on strategic grounds. There was always plenty to do much nearer home, and nobody ever considered that there could be any possible threat to the continent's security from the north. It is only in the past twenty years that this attitude has changed and the strategic importance of the Arctic has become obvious.

*The author is here expressing his own views rather than those of the Canadian Government.

The defence of Canada must be considered as part of the defence of the North American continent as a whole. This was made clear by President Roosevelt's statement at Kingston, Ontario, in 1938: "I give to you assurance that the people of the United States will not stand idly by if domination of Canadian soil is threatened . . ." and by Mr. Mackenzie King's reply at Woodbridge, Ontario, two days later when he expressed Canada's obligation to see that "our country is made as secure from attack or possible invasion as we can reasonably be expected to make it, and that, should the occasion ever arise, enemy forces should not be able to pursue their way, either by land, sea or air to the United States across Canadian territory." Two years later the Permanent Joint Board on Defence, consisting of equivalent United States and Canadian sections, was created, and it has continued to meet regularly ever since to discuss and advise on common problems of defence.

During the Second World War many of the Permanent Joint Board on Defence's recommendations were concerned with northern Canada, and as a result projects on a scale far surpassing anything seen before in the North were initiated. The threat of Japanese attack and Japanese operations in the Aleutians led to four major undertakings: the Alaska Highway was built from Dawson Creek to Fairbanks to provide a land route to Alaska, and in this way great areas of the north-west were for the first time made accessible; the Caltel telegraph line along the route of the Alaska Highway provided reliable telecommunications with Alaska; the Canadian airfields in north-west Canada were expanded and, as the North-West Staging Route, were used for delivery of aircraft to Alaska and Russia; and the Canol project covered not only construction of the major pipeline and the Canol road between the oil field at Norman Wells and Whitehorse, but also subsidiary pipelines from Whitehorse to Skagway, Watson Lake and Fairbanks, an oil exploration programme in the Norman Wells area, a refinery at Whitehorse, and improved transportation facilities in the Mackenzie valley.   All of these projects have made important contributions to the development of north-west Canada and, with the exception of Canol, are still in use. In north-east Canada the war in Europe led to the construction of a number of airfields known as the Crimson Staging Route.   They were scarcely used for their original purpose of providing a ferry route for short-range aircraft to Europe, but they have contributed very greatly to the rapid post-war increase of flying and other developments in the Eastern Arctic.

In 1944 Canada reimbursed the United States for the cost of all works of permanent value on the war-time airfields in northern Canada, for the Caltel telegraph line, and for certain transportation facilities.   By the terms under which it was built the Canadian part of the Alaska Highway reverted to Canadian control shortly after the end of the war, while the Canol Project, which was found to have no permanent defence value, and could not be operated as an economic proposition, has for the most part been dismantled.

Though it was actually carried out after the war, the attempt to establish low-frequency loran (long range) coverage in the Arctic as an aid to air navigation sprang out of war-time developments of this type of navigation system. Stations were established in the Western Arctic but technical difficulties were too great to justify continued peacetime operation.

With the end of the Second World War it might have been expected that the Canadian North would lose much of its importance to defence, but instead it assumed new significance.   A map of the northern hemisphere based on a polar projection shows the reason for this. The Polar Basin lies between the great land masses of the world, and the great powers and possible great powers—North America, Western Europe, Russia, and Eastern Asia. Until comparatively recently the Arctic Ocean, with its perennial polar ice pack as an effective obstacle to surface shipping, was a complete barrier, but this is no longer true owing to the rapid development of long-range aviation during and since the war. The second world war left the U.S.A. and the U.S.S.R. as the two most powerful nations. The Canadian Arctic lies between them and if hostilities were to break out, Canada would necessarily be involved.

Geographically the Canadian Arctic is of great potential strategic importance. The measures necessary to defend an area must depend on an assessment of the nature and extent of possible enemy action against it. Within the north there is little in the way of developed resources to make it important in itself. The uranium mine at Port Radium on Great Bear Lake would seem to be the only economic target which might be considered of strategic significance. It is, of course, as an avenue of approach to the industrial regions of North America that the Canadian North assumes importance. This importance is increased by each improvement in the capabilities of long-range bomber aircraft. So long as it could be assumed that enemy aircraft would carry conventional bombs only, the possibility of a major blow being struck in this way was comparatively remote. The material results which could be achieved would be small in relation to the inevitably heavy losses of aircraft and the difficulties involved, and the most likely purpose of such a raid would be to divert a disproportionate effort in men and equipment away from a primary theatre, as had been done so successfully by the Japanese in their Aleutian campaign. The knowledge that the Russians were able to manufacture atomic bombs, and their more recent success with hydrogen bombs has, however, made the possibility of a bomber attack on North America a much more real threat.

The defence of North America from air attack from the north presents a number of major problems. The Canadian Arctic is an immense area. The provision of air defences on a scale adequate to defend the whole area would require an enormous effort. The cost of the U.S.A.F. base at Thule, which is comparatively accessible by sea, gives some measure of the order of expenditure which would be needed to establish conventional airfields for modern fighter aircraft. Each field in the Canadian Arctic, where transportation problems are far greater, would entail considerably larger installation and maintenance costs. It does not appear practicable, therefore, to meet and fight enemy raids with aircraft stationed at a number of major bases in the far north. Interceptor forces would be far more effectively employed nearer to the targets in the populated areas, where facilities are much less costly to install and maintain.

A great deal of interest has been aroused recently by proposals to establish a chain of radar stations across the far north of Canada. Many advantages are claimed to justify such a chain. Several hours warning would be given before bombers appeared over heavily populated areas. This would enable the fighter defences to be made ready and would give time for civil defence measures including the evacuation of major cities. The chain itself would admittedly be very vulnerable to any attack, but the attack itself would be a warning, and it is held that it would be worthwhile solely as a measure of insurance against a sudden onslaught of the Pearl Harbour pattern.

Against these attractive, if somewhat oversimplified, advantages there are, as General of the Army Omar Bradley has pointed out, a number of weighty objections. The north presents many technical as well as logistic problems, and the cost of a radar chain would be very great indeed. An unreliable warning system would be worse than no system at all, and the Maginot Line is a lesson against putting too much faith in a static system of defence which loses its value when it is once broken.

Apart from the likelihood of false alarms, each of which would cause a major disruption of normal life throughout North America, an enemy would be able to mount purposely abortive raids in which aircraft would penetrate the chain, set in motion the elaborate and costly defence measures, and then fly back to their bases. Alternatively some of the enemy aircraft could return to base, giving the impression of a feint attack, while others went on to their targets.

The full value of radar is only realized when enemy aircraft can be tracked continuously so that their course and speed can be determined, revealing their objectives and assisting fighter aircraft to engage them. There is much to be said therefore for building radar outwards from the areas they protect to give continuous tracking, rather than establishing a single line on the periphery of the continent, which might give unconfirmed warnings but nothing else. The distance to which such continuous radar coverage could be pushed north would depend on the amount of effort which it was considered justifiable to spend, the cost increasing with each step north. In this connection it should be remembered that conventional radar coverage will be of little assistance in warning against rocket-type guided missiles of the V2 family, when these have been given sufficient range for trans-polar use.

The importance of the air force and of air defence in northern Canada overshadows that of the other fighting services, but they too have a part to play. In their Alaskan campaign the Japanese, with a small commitment at Attu and Kiska Islands and a few roaming submarines, were successful in forcing the United States and Canada to retain on the west coast and in Alaska naval, army, and air forces very many times greater than their own. This strategy might well be employed by an enemy in northern Canada, where small detachments could be landed and supplied by air. Such detachments would be most easily neutralized before they could become well established, and as long as they existed they would be a potential source of danger through the support they might afford to enemy bombers by assisting navigation, by passing meteorological reports, and possibly by providing refuelling facilities. They could also seize and destroy weather stations and other installations of defence value in the north.

There is an important role for the air force in locating such detachments and for the army in destroying them. It is here too that the Canadian Ranger force could be of service in detecting and observing enemy activity as well as in supplying guides and local information. In order to cover so vast an area, mobility is all-important and airborne troops are obviously essential. The soldier must also be able to move on the ground, a very hard requirement to meet especially during the break-up and freeze-up periods, while the difficulties caused by the severe climate, the lack of local facilities, the problems of concealment, and the arctic terrain, demand a high standard of training and leadership at all levels. Improvements in equipment, especially over-snow vehicles, and in tactics will lessen these difficulties but it would be rash to assume that the enemy would not be equally well or better prepared for northern operations.

An obvious responsibility of naval forces in the defence of Canada is the security of sea supply routes to military installations in the Arctic, including weather stations which provide meteorological information essential to air oper-ations. Icebreakers will be required owing to the ice conditions, but there is also the need for protection against enemy attacks. While the movement of escort vessels is more difficult in northern waters, submarines are able to operate there with comparative freedom. Even during the Second World War the presence of ice was not considered a deterrent, and German submarines were used in the Svalbard area and other northern waters. It became in fact a practice to paint them white as an aid to concealment among the ice floes. With their ability to evade pursuit by diving under the ice where they cannot be followed, sub-marines would be able to harass shipping most effectively. It is also not beyond the bounds of possibility that they would be used to land and support raiding parties on im-portant installations in the Arctic. The task of locating and destroying enemy submarines would not be an easy one for thin-skinned vessels, and icebreaker support would at times be essential.

Many defence activities in the Canadian North are of incalculable value to the civilian population and to the future development of the country. The Northwest Territories and Yukon Signals System of the Royal Can-adian Corps of Signals provides radio communications for much of the North, particularly the Yukon Territory and the District of Mackenzie. The Army Survey Establish-ment produces many of the northern map sheets and sends parties into the north to obtain data required for these maps. The Royal Canadian Air Force has covered virtually all the Arctic with tricamera photography and many areas with vertical photography. The most important use of these photographs is for compilation of detailed maps, but they also contain information of the greatest value to explorers, engineers, foresters, geologists, and other scientists. In addition the Air Force operates northern airfields which are used by civil as well as military air transport, and supports many of the activities of government departments in the Arctic. They co-operate with the Department of Mines and Technical Surveys in obtaining shoran and astronomical control essential for accurate mapping, and in investigations of terrestrial magnetism, such as the series of flights undertaken to locate the current position of the North Magnetic Pole. For the Department of Transport they provide airlift for the far northern weather stations and carry out ice reconnaissance to assist shipping. Several other government scientific investigations have been dependent on Royal Canadian Air Force help, and the whole north is in their debt for their many mercy flights and deliveries of urgently needed supplies and mail to isolated posts.

In all military operations in the North the difficulties of defence spring from two main factors. One is the special conditions of the Arctic and the restrictions they impose on men and equipment; the other is the small local population and the consequent lack of men with practical experience of conditions as well as the absence of communications and other facilities within the country. The effect of arctic conditions can be countered to some extent by research and by training, but there is little doubt that the further development of the north, leading to an increase in population, resources, communications, and other facilities, would be a most important contribution to defence.

Index